MINES OF DEVON

MINES OF DEVON

Volume I

THE SOUTHERN AREA

A. K. HAMILTON JENKIN

DAVID & CHARLES
NEWTON ABBOT LONDON
NORTH POMFRET (VT) VANCOUVER

ISBN o 7153 6784 6

Library of Congress Catalog Card Number

© A. K. Hamilton Jenkin 1974

Set in 11 on 13 Baskerville and printed in
Great Britain by John Sherratt and Son Ltd
St Ann's Press, Park Road, Altrincham, Cheshire WA14 5QQ
for David & Charles (Holdings) Limited
South Devon House Newton Abbot Devon

Published in the United States of America
by David & Charles Inc North Pomfret
Vermont 05053 USA

Published in Canada by Douglas David &
Charles Limited 3645 McKechnie Drive
West Vancouver BC

CONTENTS

CONTENTS

LIST OF ILLUSTRATIONS

PLATES

LIST OF ILLUSTRATIONS

IN TEXT

ABBREVIATIONS

Collins   Collins, J. H. *Observations on the West of England Mining Region* (1912)

CRO   County Record Office

Dines   Dines, H. G. *The Metalliferous Mining Region of South-West England* Vols 1-2 (1956)

MJ   *Mining Journal* (1835 onwards)

Murchison   Murchison, J. H. *British Mines Considered as a Means of Investment* (1854)

RIC   Royal Institution of Cornwall

Spargo   Spargo, Thomas. *The Mines of Cornwall and Devon* (1868 ed)

Other books and sources cited in the text will be found in the Notes and Sources (pp 143-9).

The term fathom (6ft/1·829m) is used throughout, this being until recently the standard measure of length and depth common to all West Country mines.

INTRODUCTION

In recent years the growing appeal of industrial archaeology
has reawakened interest in the subject of mining in Devon.
The first fruits of this was seen in the publication by Mr Frank
Booker of his now standard work on the mining and industries
of the Tamar Valley. Since then further contributions have
appeared on the Birch Tor tin complex of Dartmoor and the
lead mines of the Teign Valley. Valuable as these special
studies have proved, the fact remains that no book has yet been
written on the mines of Devon as a whole, although the need
for such a work has long been recognised. Having waited in
vain for some Devon historian to supply this need it has now
fallen to me, a Cornishman, to attempt the task.

Among the countless number of visitors who pour into the
West Country each summer, few realise that Devon once
possessed a metal mining industry almost as diversified as that
of Cornwall, although in general on a much smaller scale. In
1862 100 mines are known to have been at work and as late as
1870 the number was not less than sixty. In addition to these
the heyday of the industry witnessed an incalculable number
of prospecting trials, many of which are described for the first
time in this book.

That tin has been worked in Cornwall since the Bronze Age
is now generally agreed. Less well known is the fact that for a
period in the Middle Ages the greater part of the metal supplying the needs of Europe and the Near East was derived from
the alluvial gravels of Dartmoor where from a mere sixty tons
in 1156 production rose to over 340 tons a year between 1171
and 1189. By the thirteenth century, however, the richest
deposits of the moor were showing signs of exhaustion and the

main centre reverted to Cornwall which thenceforth maintained its predominance until, in the sixteenth century, alluvial 'streaming' gradually gave way to the beginnings of underground mining. In this new development Devon played only a minor role, the county possessing no tin lodes comparable in size and productiveness to those of Cornwall.

In lead and silver mining Devon was early to the forefront. Exploitation of the argentiferous lead ores of Combe Martin was already in full swing in the reign of Edward I when it is recorded that over 300 men were brought down from Derbyshire to work them. For a considerable period the mines proved very productive and according to Lysons provided funds for the wars of Edward III. They were still active in 1485, but a few years later were said to be 'deep and almost worn out'. Reopened in the reign of Elizabeth fresh deposits were discovered, but the ore was found difficult to treat and on reaching a depth of 32 fathoms values showed a falling off. Subsequent trials initiated during the last century had little or no success.

During the thirteenth and fourteenth centuries the mining of silver-lead was similarly pursued under royal patronage in the Bere Alston peninsula in the south-west of the county. Operations are known to have been started here by 1290 and four years later it is recorded that 370lb of refined silver was sent up to London from Martinstow (now Maristow) near the mouth of the Tavy. Between 1292 and 1297 returns amounted to £4,000 worth of silver and £360 of lead, the maximum output apparently being reached in 1305 when the exports of silver and lead were valued at £1,773 and £180 respectively. These figures should be multiplied by at least 120 to give some idea of their worth in present-day money values.

During the above period large numbers of miners were drafted into the region from the Peak District of Derbyshire and also from Wales. By 1340, however, the boom years were over, although working continued on a reduced scale until nearly the end of the fifteenth century. After this the Bere mines lapsed into obscurity and remained dormant until their revival in the eighteenth century.

In copper mining Devon was a late starter compared with Cornwall where the industry was already well established by the middle of the eighteenth century. Although trials had been made for copper in the North Molton area during the latter part of the seventeenth century, and some years later on the banks of the Tamar and Tavy, the output at that period was insignificant. As late as the year 1801 production in Devon totalled little more than 1,000 tons and although this had risen to over 6,000 tons by 1837 it still lagged far behind Cornwall where sales in those years amounted to 56,611 and 140,753 tons respectively. By 1840 returns showed a considerable increase mainly due to the rapid growth of Devon Friendship Mine which from 1800 to 1885 yielded ores in excess of 155,000 tons.

Meantime in 1844 work had started at Devon Great Consols which in the course of the next twenty years was destined to become the richest copper mine in Europe, with an output of 736,000 tons of ore valued at more than £3 million sterling. In its later years the mine had the further distinction of being one of the world's largest producers of arsenic. The spectacular achievements of Devon Great Consols stimulated the search for copper throughout the county. Although few of the mines resulting from this proved outstandingly rich, their combined output led to a peak production of 41,513 tons in 1862. Whilst this was no mean achievement, it was wholly eclipsed by that of Cornwall where a maximum output of 198,697 tons was attained in 1857.

In this and a succeeding volume, which will cover the northern part of the county, I have followed the plan outlined in my earlier work, *Mines and Miners of Cornwall*. In the case of the larger and better-known mines I have confined myself for the most part to adding only information antedating anything previously known of their history. My main preoccupation has been with the numerous small and now forgotten mines whose names and sites are not to be found in any readily available source. It is these which reveal the climate of the time when Devon ranked as a field of mining enterprise to an extent unrecognised today. Many of these small and ephemeral trials owed their inception to some trifling incident, a typical instance being that of Devon Burra Burra where the chance discovery of a gatepost showing traces of copper awakened a speculative fever of excitement which extended even to the City of London.

Having recounted the history of such mines, every effort has been made to locate them in the field. Wherever this has proved possible their sites have been noted in my own set of the 6in OS maps (2nd ed c1906), but the reproduction of these is unfortunately prohibited by reason of cost. Instead – as far as is feasible – grid references are given so that they may be found on the 2½in scale maps, but, of course, the scene is liable to change fast under the impact of new roadworks, building development and local council 'improvement' schemes.

Furthermore, Devon has long been conspicuously neglectful of the physical structures relating to its industrial past. Although endowed with far fewer engine-houses than Cornwall, it possessed at Wheal Exmouth two of the most sumptuous and imposing buildings of their kind ever erected in England. So far from placing any value on these in 1956 an order was made by the local council for their demolition on the trumped-up excuse of their being dangerous. A contractor was engaged to carry out the work but so fortress-like were the engine-houses that the attempt was soon abandoned and though sadly mutilated, the buildings still remain.

A few years later the finely proportioned engine-house and stack of West Crebor Mine, for long a conspicuous landmark on the heights above the Tamar, was senselessly destroyed; the engine-house of Wheal Betsy, now happily in the guardian-

14

ship of the National Trust, was only saved from a like fate by the timely intervention of the present writer.

Due to its abundant water-power, Devon formerly owned more water-wheels than any other county in the West of England, a number of them being of outstanding size – 50, 60 and in one instance 70ft in diameter. Of these magnificent specimens of the former millwrights' art not one survives today.

In a book of this sort it is usual to make acknowledgements to a host of people who have contributed to its writing. In my case the number has been few and my indebtedness to them has for that very reason been all the greater. Foremost I would mention Mr Frank Booker who, in addition to checking my manuscript and preparing sketch maps, has been ready at all times to assist and encourage me with sound advice. My very special thanks are also due to Mr Justin Brooke, who has relieved me of the task of making an index and list of grid references, besides sharing with my cousin Ruth Phillips the typing of portions of my manuscript. To my friend Geoffrey Ordish I am once again indebted for allowing me to draw on his photographic collection of the mining scene which for the greater part of a lifetime has been a labour of love complementary to my own. Finally I wish to acknowledge the personal interest shown in my work by Mr David St John Thomas of David & Charles, but for whom this book would probably never have been written.

A. K. Hamilton Jenkin

Trewirgie House, Redruth
February 1974

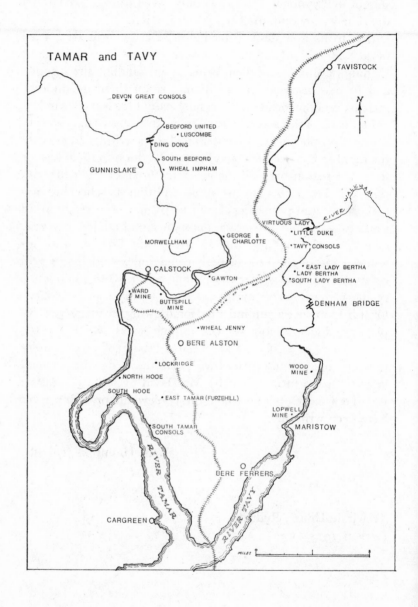

PART ONE

TAMAR and TAVY

TAMAR AND TAVY

No book purporting to be a record of mining in Devon could be regarded as complete without some reference to the most celebrated of all its mines – Devon Great Consols. The account that follows is condensed by Frank Booker from his standard work on the area, *The Industrial Archaeology of the Tamar Valley* (1967):

The A390 road out of Tavistock climbs over Morwell Down to dip steeply to the Tamar and cross into Cornwall at Gunnislake over a sixteenth-century bridge. Looking northwards from the bridge, a swell of land bordered by the river rises to above the 200ft contour. Although now thick with trees, glimpses can be seen of sandy dumps and heaps of calcined waste. This is the famous Blanchdown Wood (SX426733), the site of Devon Great Consols Mine, once the richest copper working in Europe. In less than sixty years it produced 736,000 tons of copper ore and 72,000 tons of refined arsenic.

The story of Devon Great Consols is one of the great romances of West Country mining, but the apparent chance discovery of copper at Blanchdown in November 1844 obscures the fact that there had long been suspicions of it in the neighbourhood. The site was littered with 'good gossan', a cindery-looking stone indicating the weathered back of a copper lode. The presence of copper in the area seems certainly to have been known since Elizabethan times. William Carnsew in his memoranda c1580 mentions copper on the borders of Devon and refers particularly to an occurrence 'at Tavistock' surpassing all that he had seen both in value and quantity – three men being able to break more than a ton of such ore per week. Eight tons of it, he says, produce one ton of copper (metal). Carnsew then goes on to say that of the several lodes the largest and most valuable is 'next the bridge'. If one assumes this to be Gunnislake bridge, the temptation to associate these lodes with those of Blanchdown is strong. But we really do not know. Carnsew's remarks might equally well refer to deposits later worked at Ding Dong or more probably Bedford United Mine, adjoining Devon Great Consols and where the so-called Marquis Lode was being explored long before Devon Great Consols began working. The existence, then, of rich mineral wealth in the area had long been known, and on the Blanch-down site widely suspected. The trouble with the latter had been getting the Duke of Bedford's consent to work it.

On 25 March 1844 permission was secured by Josiah Hugo Hitchins, a Tavistock mineral agent of great mining skill and foresight. Hitchins brought off his coup in the face of stiff competition from other mining interests, among them the Williams family of Scorrier who had developed Old Gunnislake Mine close by on the Tamar's Cornish bank. The mine had earlier interested the Williams family but their overtures had been rebuffed by the 6th Duke of Bedford with the remark that 'he did not want a gang of miners disturbing his pheasant coverts'.

Hitchins, with a lease in his pocket stipulating that at least £20,000 must be spent in developing the site and that the duke's royalty should be one-twelfth, rapidly formed a joint stock company with five other people of 1,024 shares of which he took 144.

The Blanchdown sett was 3 miles long and 2 miles wide and contained what was to prove the longest sulphide lode in the West of England. On its extreme western edge was an oak coppice in which there already existed an old overgrown shaft 14 fathoms deep, reputed to have been sunk by Hitchins's father and known as North Wheal Bedford. Under the supervision of Captain James Phillips, manager for many years of the adjoining Bedford United mine in which Hitchins was a shareholder, work began on 10 August 1844 by clearing the shaft and digging a line of costeaning pits. By 4 November the shaft had been sunk a further 2½ fathoms. Late in that afternoon there was a sudden inrush of water and the back of a 30ft wide copper lode was revealed. By the time the working shift ended at 10 o'clock that night £60 worth of ore had been recovered. The lode yielded 17 per cent of copper (metal) at a time when the average yield in Devon and Cornwall was 7¾ per cent. The new working was named Wheal Maria, after Hitchins's wife, and the shaft, marked by a stone today, became known as Gard's Shaft – after Richard Gard, MP for Exeter and a London discount broker, who was an early subscriber.

Work on proving the lode was pushed eastwards for 16 fathoms when, to everyone's consternation, it was suddenly lost, having been heaved to the right by a geological fault. It was soon found again, however, and developed east of the fault as Wheal Fanny, so called after Hitchins's infant daughter. As the strike of the lode was traced still further eastwards, other mines were established on it. These became Wheal Anna Maria, in honour of the Duchess of Bedford; Wheal Josiah (after Hitchins himself); and finally at the eastern extremity of the lode Wheal Emma, named after Mrs Morris, the wife of another shareholder. In 1845 the entire complex became known as Devon Great Consols, a title which included two subsidiary workings – South Wheal Fanny and Watson's Mine, south of Wheal Emma.

By the end of 1845 the main lode had been proved for almost its entire length of two miles. In the first full year of working, a profit of £73,622 was made and dividends of £72,704 or £71 a share were paid. The asking price of an original £1 share (which some Tavistock tradespeople had initially thought too risky to buy) was now £800.

As the mine developed, it became clear that the copper deposits deepened as they went eastwards. At Wheal Maria, on the western boundary, copper was found above the drainage adit, and between the 10 and 30 fathom levels the shoots of ore were often up to 30ft wide. At Wheal Fanny a shoot extended from surface to 55 fathoms. At Wheal Josiah lode values were found only below 50 fathoms, and at Wheal Emma between 60 and 130 fathoms. The lode in many places was embedded in arsenopyrite or mispickel which was later to be mined in quantity as arsenic. The little riverside quay of Morwellham, five miles down the Tamar, whence all the ore was sent to South Wales for smelting, was taxed to its utmost limits and additional quay space had to be improvised hurriedly at Newquay and at Gawton further down the river.

A small water-wheel had been adequate to drain the shallow Gard's Shaft, but as the lode deepened pumping and other costs increased, causing the dividend to fall in 1847 to £25 a share and immediately giving rise to rumours that the mine was on the point of collapse. In fact, its riches were only just beginning to be exploited. Four steam pumping engines were installed in 1847, but the mine became more remarkable for its use of water-power. In 1849 on the advice of Nathaniel Smith, chief engineer of the Devon Friendship Mine which was noted for its large water-wheels, it was decided to harness the Tamar for pumping and crushing wherever possible. A two-mile leat was cut from the river upstream near Latchley which eventually powered two 40ft water-wheels. From these flat rods, supported on wooden trestles, draining shafts at Wheal Maria and Wheal Josiah extended uphill for nearly three-quarters of a mile. Turning at 4rpm, this massive assemblage of hydraulic gear worked at about 60 per cent efficiency. A plunger wheel also pumped water from the Tamar to feed a reservoir and storage ponds on the higher parts of the mine, while a 35ft by 4ft wheel drove the machinery at the mine's own foundry. Altogether the river water powered thirty-three wheels, and for the first twenty years the company paid the Duchy of Cornwall £200 a year for its abstraction. This meant that in its most prosperous period the company's basic source of power cost less than £5 a week.

Throughout the fifties and into the middle sixties the wealth of the mine was a byword, and as 'rich as Devon Great Consols' became the yardstick by which every other mining prospect in the area was measured and compared. The lode at Wheal Maria was 47ft wide and produced 60 tons of ore a running fathom. At Wheal Anna Maria, where the ore occurred in two shoots, most of the lode was removed throughout the full length of the sett between the 60 and 124 fathom levels. In the mine's first twelve years of working, ore sales realised £1,400,000 or £35,000 more than Dolcoath's total output in the forty years after Waterloo. In ten years dividends totalled over £475,000, and it was estimated in 1855 that there were sufficient reserves (35,943 tons) to keep the mine going for over a year without fresh discoveries. By 1857 the Duke of Bedford had received over £100,000 in dues and had even been paid £2,050 for the despoilation of his pheasant coverts.

On the other hand, the softness of the lode and its walls made it expensive to work. Underhand stoping, instead of the more usual and easier overhead method, had to be adopted. Ore extracted from one section left a cavity 900ft long, 240ft wide and 6ft to 50ft high – the dimensions of a small cathedral. To offset frequent runs of ground, which caused a number of fatalities, massive timbering was introduced. For this, special timber from the Baltic and Canadian Pacific coasts had to be imported, costing the company an average of £4,000 a year.

By the late 1850s the expense of haulage to and from Morwellham and the lack of quay space there (ore was often washed into the river when the Tamar flooded) forced the company to undertake a twofold development. Horse and cart hire to Morwellham was costing 5s a ton and in 1854 amounted to £6,000. This was more than the working profits of many small mines. It was also slow and difficult, and on the steep approach down to Morwellham the steel skid shoes under the wheels of the laden wagons became so hot that carters were said to be able to fry fatty bacon in them. To replace this cartage a 4½ mile standard-gauge railway was built and opened in 1858, costing £10,355 which the company paid for out of current income, an impressive tribute to its financial stability. The railway (powered by steam) ran from Wheal Maria, with access tracks to the other mines, to a point above Morwellham from where trucks were let down over a half mile 1 in 3 incline.

On the quay itself £5,000 was spent excavating a new dock able to hold six 300 ton vessels. At the same time several acres of new quays were reclaimed from the mud, and staging built over them to allow the 3½ ton ore trucks with sliding bottoms to empty their lodes into piles directly on the quays. All the quays were tiled to prevent any loss of ore, and were regularly swept. Extra cottages, still eagerly sought-after today, were built by the Duke of Bedford to house miners and dock workers, while the landlord of the Ship Inn (noted among sailors and visitors alike for its 'roast beef of old England and stout October ale') also found it necessary to enlarge his premises. Henceforth Morwellham, which probably handled over 36,000 tons of ore, mine supplies and other cargo a year, became an integral part of the mine.

By 1865 the surface area of the mines sprawled over more than 140 acres. The four principal lodes were Main, Middle Lode, South Lode (the latter branching off from the main lode at Wheal Anna Maria and uniting with it again at Wheal Josiah) and New South Lode, first cut in 1864 and worked by Wheal Emma. There were some fifteen shafts, the deepest being Richards' (230 fathoms) at Wheal Josiah where four of the chief lodes were worked. It took an hour to climb to surface from Richards' Shaft. There were 40 miles of levels and it was possible to walk uninterruptedly underground for 2½ miles between the extreme western and eastern boundaries of the sett. Whilst over 1,000 men, women and children were employed (a school with a paid mistress was provided on the mine for children too young to work), it was estimated the mine gave indirect employment to over 6,000 people. The mine had its own brass band and supplied a choir, widely renowned, for Ogbeare Methodist Chapel, which adjoined the mine site.

In 1864 the company paid its fourth highest dividend (£62 a share) and raised 26,947 tons of copper ore. By the end of the decade, however, there were signs that the immensely rich copper lodes were becoming exhausted. The main lode had been stoped almost continuously for much of its course. South Lode at Wheal Josiah, which had yielded very nearly £600,000, ended in barren ground at 144 fathoms. In 1872 only 16,329 tons of ore were produced, making £6,144 available for dividend. The company, in common with other mines in Devon and Cornwall, also began to face competition from Australian and American mines producing copper more cheaply from shallower deposits. In the late 1860s there was also a slump in copper prices. To offset these factors the company turned its attention to the treatment of its large dumps of low-grade ore and to the mundic or arsenopyrite which had been left standing, sometimes up to a fathom or more in width, beside the copper stopes.

This decision was also influenced by an increasing commercial demand for arsenic not only in England but also from the expanding German chemical industry. Arsenic was the principal constituent of Emerald Green and King's Yellow, both fast, strong and extremely brilliant dyes. It was also used in paint and in the glass industry. Also about this time, the first man-made insecticide was perfected. This was Paris Green, a compound of gypsum and arsenic which proved initially so successful against the cotton boll weevil and Colorado potato beetle that for a time mankind dreamed of totally eliminating insect pests. Arsenic reduction works, capable of dealing with

2,500 tons a year, were completed at Wheal Maria in 1871 and progressively enlarged until they covered eight acres. They were the largest such works in Devon and Cornwall. An unusual feature was the later use in these works of the Oxland tubular calciner as opposed to the generally adopted Brunton pyramid type. The first sales of arsenic were made in 1868. By 1871 it was providing up to 20 per cent of the mine's receipts, and by the middle 1870s the company boasted that it was producing half the United Kingdom's arsenic.

The decision to prolong the mine's life by exploiting its rich arsenic deposits was supplemented by two attempts to find tin beneath the copper zone. This had happened at Dolcoath Mine, and conditions at Devon Great Consols were thought to be similar. In the hope of making the mine a Devonshire Dolcoath, the company was financially reconstructed and Richards' Shaft at Wheal Josiah (chosen because it was nearest the granite) was deepened in the early 1870s from 230 to 300 fathoms, but without any tin being found. In 1883 a second attempt was made in the adjoining Wheal Emma sett where tin stones had been found in Railway Shaft. With the aid of rock drills this shaft was carried down from 205 to 260 fathoms but again without any success. The total reward from these two expensive operations was a mere £170 worth of tin.

Arsenic now became the mainstay of the mine for its remaining years which were clouded by the increasing unwillingness of the Duke of Bedford to co-operate with the board (although he consented to forego £1,000 of his dues in 1885), and board-room squabbles stemming from opposition to the financial policies of Mr Peter Watson, a Redruth mining personality of bluff, John Bull-like appearance, who had become managing director in 1879. Copper by now had become little more than a by-product; by 1890 the mine was selling three times as much arsenic as copper. Between 1890 and 1891 the total 'make' of arsenic was 5,883 4cwt barrels which in the following year was increased to over 6,000 barrels.

INCLINE SHAFT MAIN ENGINE THOMAS SHAFT INCLINE

RAILWAY SHAFT

Page 25
(*above*) Wheal Emma, the last discovered and most easterly extension of the Devon Great Consols complex. This is the only known picture showing features of the surface workings in any detail;
(*below*) miners' cottages at Wheal Josiahs Tavistock

Page 26

(*above*) Oxland tube arsenic calciner at Devon Great Consols – the bearded man is probably Captain Isaac Richards; (*below*) one of the few surface remains of South Hooe silver-lead mine. This is the auction window of the old count-house from which pitches were sold to tributers

Page 27
(*left*) Arsenic stack,
Wheal Josiah, Devon
Great Consols Mine,
believed to have been
built in the early 1920s
when part of the mine
was reopened for arsenic
working

(*right*) shaft head gear
and tram road at
Bedford United Mine,
probably taken in the
early 1920s

Morwellham, probably between 1890 and 1900 at a time when the port was beginning to fall into decay. The large dock in the foreground is already showing signs of silting up

Although the whole concern was now in debt and the labour force had been reduced to under 400, there were still cosy and jovial parties on the mine whenever the directors made their annual inspection. In October 1899, when the mine had only two more years to run, Captain William Woolcock, in charge of Wheal Emma, records a 'very nice dinner' for directors and shareholders of 'boiled leg of mutton at the head of the table, ribs of beef at the bottom, two steak pies in the middle with plain dumplings after and apples, pears and grapes for dessert' all washed down by a 'liberal supply of claret'. The meal was cooked in the count house kitchen.

In that year the mine paid its last dividend – 2s 6d a share. By 1901 a steady decline in the price of arsenic and the high price of coal had led to a loss of nearly £3,000 in the previous two years working, and the company, which had borrowed £9,000 in 1898 to cover its losses for that year, owed its bankers nearly £4,000. On 30 November 1901, all work ceased except for pumping in the upper levels and the company went into voluntary liquidation. In a last effort to get the mine working again, Mr Watson called in Captain W. H. Borlase who estimated the value of ore in sight at £57,000 and recommended a better application of the enormous water-power available and the provision of cage roads in the shafts. This scheme was defeated by a lobby antagonistic to the chairman and in May 1903 the mines were abandoned and all the materials sold off.

With their closure, the little port of Morwellham, its quays now deserted and its great dock silting up, died also.

On its south, Devon Great Consols is adjoined by Bedford United Mine (OS 105 SW). Although not equalling the extraordinary richness of its neighbour, the Bedford United was a highly productive sett with a recorded output of 66,000 tons of copper ore, in addition to smaller quantities of arsenic, tin and, latterly, wolfram. While generally assumed to have been started in the early 1840s, the mine, in fact, originated in the opening years of the eighteenth century, as is related by Henrik Kahlmeter, a Swedish engineer, who visited the site on 13 November 1724.[1]

'In the wood called Collingswood,' Kahlmeter records, certain workmen in 1707 obtained a lease of land from the Duke of Bedford extending 20 fathoms from the River Tamar and thence up the rising ground to the east. Here they drove an adit, and finding copper named this part of the sett the Bedford Mine. Shortly afterwards a wealthier group of adventurers obtained another sett higher up the hillside where they started a second adit seven or eight fathoms above the first and drove it 60 fathoms. Subsequently the two workings were amalgamated and became known as the Marquis Mine. On commencing the upper adit, tin was met with near the outcrop of the lode, but on excavating deeper copper was encountered in considerable quantity and of better grade than in the first adit. At length the water gained on the workmen to such an extent that sixty men were required to drain it (presumably by means of rag-and-chain pumps) until this became too costly and the working was abandoned for some years.

In 1722 the mine was acquired by the Bristol Copper Company who erected an underground engine near the adit end. This was driven by water directed down a shaft from surface which, after passing over a pumping wheel, flowed out through the adit mouth. By such means the Company contrived to sink the shaft 39 fathoms below the adit, effectively draining the workings to that level. The lode ran due east–west and varied in width from 1 to 4ft. At the time of Kahlmeter's visit, twenty miners were employed at a wage of 28s a month 'including free tools and lights', whilst the smith received 25s and the carpenter 40s. On being brought to surface, the ore was hammered clear of stone and impurities and then sent two miles by road to Nuttstack[2] on the Tamar. Here it was shipped to Plymouth and thence to Bristol or alternatively to the smelting house at Neath in South Wales. By way of a footnote Kahlmeter adds that close by the Marquis there was another copper lode called the Tavistock but this had not been worked 'for the last seven years'.

The Bedford United sett in its later form commenced working in 1841 when it included the lodes of Wheal Marquis, Wheal Tavistock, Delves Kitchen, Ding Dong and South Bedford. Delves Kitchen is known to have been worked before 1799 and by 1844 had been developed for 200 fathoms at adit level, 24 fathoms below surface. The Ding Dong lode lay parallel with this and is referred to in a letter of 19 September 1807 from William Jenkin of Trewirgie, Redruth, to his friend William Phillips, mineralogist and publisher of George Yard, Lombard Street:

> I have just received from Captain Davey his report on the Ding Dong Mine on the Devonshire side of the Tamar. He says 'tis a rich lode in Mundick, with some copper ore intermixed with it – and it being a gozan lode with those appearances, he thinks it deserves a tryal. He did not express himself very strongly – as if he thought highly of it but repeated, as before mentioned, that he thought it deserved some tryal.

By 1844 the lode had been opened up by an adit which was 42 fathoms from surface at its deepest point, and below this by a shaft drained by a 45ft water-wheel.[3]

On starting work on the northern part of the Bedford sett it was found that the lodes had been entirely worked away by the old men for a length of 200 fathoms and down to the deep adit (47 fathoms). In 1843 levels were being driven at 25, 30 and 40 fathoms below adit on the Marquis Lode where a 50ft pumping wheel had been erected. To drive this and the wheel on Ding Dong Lode, water was brought through a leat from the southern end of the Tavistock Canal, high above Morwellham. From here its course can still be traced through the woods for a distance of nearly two miles, passing through two tunnels cut in the projecting rock and elsewhere carried by wooden launders slung in chains from the cliff face. After serving the needs of the mine, the leat was diverted back across the main Gunnislake–Tavistock road to convey the slimes and waste to a dump near the river.[4] In 1849 a steam-whim was erected and five shafts were in use. The deepest of these was Engine Shaft on the Tavistock Lode which followed its underlie down to an eventual depth of 150 fathoms from surface. On the Marquis Lode the shaft reached an inclined depth of 115 fathoms. Shortly after 1858 the mine was connected by a branch to the Devon Great Consols Railway over which its ores were carried at an advantageous rate to the quays at Morwellham.

In 1862 the mine was employing 200 people and by 1868 had paid dividends amounting to £54,000. The company was reconstructed in 1877 and continued in existence until 1890. Some further work was carried out above adit during the 1920s mainly for arsenic, with smaller amounts of tin and wolfram.

In Hatch Wood, about half a mile south of Gunnislake New Bridge (OS 105 SW), a number of lodes have been worked in the precipitous slopes of the Tamar and thence eastwards to Luscombe Down Plantation. These were originally developed in two separate setts, the more northerly being Wheal Luscombe (earlier spelt and pronounced Liscombe) which, according to tradition, was the first mine in Devon to possess a steam engine. In 1816 in order to facilitate drainage the workings were connected to the Ding Dong Adit, but the lode values were said to have petered out in depth on coming up against the elvan. As East Liscombe the mine returned 3,269 tons of copper ore in the years 1821 to 1834.[5]

Adjoining this on the south, Wheal Impham was a very old work referred to by Kahlmeter in 1724 as 'a copper mine out of which Mr Costar from Cornwall in four years and employing five or six men took out more than 100 tons of ore. After that values decreased – however it is now said to be better again'. A cost-book formerly in the Bedford Estate Office at Tavistock shows that the mine was still in operation during the years 1799 to 1820.

At a later period the Luscombe North and South Lodes, together with the Chimney Rock Lode of Wheal Impham, were included in the sett of Bedford United. Being too far removed from the centre of operations to be worked effectively by that company, they were transferred in 1850 to a new company called East Gunnislake and South Bedford, the former situated on the Cornwall side of the river. Between 1854 and 1871 the group returned some 5,300 tons of copper ore, with lesser amounts of pyrite and tin.

In June 1860 due to an exceptionally high tide accompanied by heavy rain, the mine was partially flooded by the water entering the adit which opened close to the river bank. By dint of working all night, a barge laden with very rich ore was manoeuvered into the Tamar Canal dock and saved, but 15 tons of ore standing on Impham Quay was swept away in the flood.

In 1868 Gard's Shaft was down to 54 fathoms below deep adit (36 fathoms), and Engine Shaft, 40yd east of the river, to 75 fathoms – in both cases on the underlie of the lode. No steam-power was employed, the water being drawn by a 36ft by 5ft wheel, with a 20ft by 5ft wheel for hoisting.[6]

The majority of lodes in this area contain a proportion of wolfram. In 1950 some exceedingly rich stones were found by the late Mr Frank Cloke in the surface filling of a lode about 800ft north-east of Impham farm house. Application was made to the Bedford Estate for a mining lease, but the terms which restricted operations to a maximum depth of 20ft being quite unacceptable, no further action was taken.

Between Morwellham and New Quay the deep adit of George and Charlotte may be seen opening on to the river bank. The mine developed the western end of a copper lode extending from the Tamar to the Tavy, a distance of nearly a mile. At its eastern extremity the lode was worked in the William and Mary Mine (OS 111 NE) which was visited by

33

Kahlmeter in 1724. According to his statement this mine was started about 1718 when 'one Lane from Bristol'[7] in conjunction with Sir William Courtenay, the mineral owner, drove a deep adit 40 fathoms from the west bank of the Tavy. When Kahlmeter saw it this level was at a standstill due to misunderstandings between the two partners.

Higher up the hill a second adit had been driven for a length of 120 fathoms and was held under grant from the Duke of Bedford at one-seventh dues. In this the lode was 4ft wide and promising in appearance. Four shafts had been sunk here but it was thought that they would have to go five or six fathoms deeper to reach the main part of the lode. No trouble was experienced from water as this was finding its way down to the deep adit. Twelve men were employed at 28s per month, with an overseer who received 40s. In the previous six months they had recovered 56 tons or '420 ship pounds' of clean ore, whilst another 30 tons was expected before Christmas, the whole worth £5 per ton on the mine. Cost of land carriage to Goton (Gawton Quay) on the Tamar was 2s 6d per ton with a further 18d per ton for sending it by boat to Plymouth. From there part of the ore was shipped to Hitchcock's smelting house in London and the rest to Neath in South Wales.

The third or topmost adit was worked by one of the Costar family from Cornwall who had sunk a winze 4 fathoms deep, but owing to the amount of the incoming water work had been suspended here until the following summer.

At what date George and Charlotte was started is not known, the earliest recorded reference to the mine being in 1806 when it was purchased as a going concern by the Tavistock Canal Company.[8] Forty years later the deep adit had been extended 130 fathoms east from the Tamar, heading towards a similar adit, then driving west from William and Mary, with the obvious intention of establishing a communication between the two mines. The lode in the George and Charlotte adit was stated at this time to be 4ft wide 'orey but not rich'.[9]

In September 1851 the two setts were amalgamated as the Devon and Cornwall United Mines – a misleading title since both its constituent parts lay wholly in Devon. During this working a number of shafts were sunk, the two deepest being Ley's (600yd west-south-west of Broadwell, to 34 fathoms below adit – here 83 fathoms from shaft collar), and Engine Shaft near the railway, to 46 fathoms under adit which at this point is 40 fathoms from surface.

In September 1866 a correspondent of *Mining Journal* wrote:

> It may not be generally known that an immense body of ore was [formerly] discovered at George & Charlotte in the deep adit, which enabled the mine to pay dividends and the huge excavations caused by its removal have been familiarly named the 'Devil's Kitchen'. A long and expensive cross-cut has been put out with a view to undermining his Satanic Majesty's cooking department which cross-cut is now near the desired object.

It would seem, however, that no downward extension of the bunch or carbona was found, and in 1869 the property was put up for sale. The machinery consisted of three water-wheels for pumping, two of 40ft diameter and one of 29ft, together with a 12in steam-whim for hoisting.

Tradition relates that after the mines had closed woodmen from the Tamar, when engaged on work in the Tavy Valley, would 'travel' through the adit in stormy weather, thus avoiding the trek over the high country between the two rivers. Although Dines states that 100 fathoms of unexplored ground separates the mines, the plans are known to be incomplete and it is more than likely that a connection formerly existed, although inaccessible today owing to rock falls.

The Bere Alston Mines
Below Gawton Mine with its leaning arsenic stack and dual refiners, the Tamar takes a westerly course past Calstock,

35

beyond which it turns abruptly south beneath the woodlands of Cotehele. Within the angle thus formed two parallel lead-bearing cross-courses strike north–south, the eastern one extending far down the Bere Alston peninsula.

At its northern end the western cross-course was developed in North Ward Mine and thence southward through Ward (or South Ward), North Hooe and South Hooe. In this last mine the lode was worked for over a quarter of a mile out beneath the bed of the river in the direction of the Cornish bank.

Some three-quarters of a mile to the east the longer eastern cross-course has been proved north–south in the mines of Buttspill, Lockridge, Furzehill, East Tamar and South Tamar, the deep levels of the latter similarly extending below the river towards Cornwall[10] (OS Cornwall 30 SW, 38 NW).

In origin, these mines are among the oldest in Britain, having been worked as early as the thirteenth century. Due to the high proportion of silver in their lodes, they ranked as royal mines and were financed by the crown which enabled them to be developed on a scale unattainable by private enterprise in the Middle Ages. Attention was called to the documents relating to the early history of the mines by Sir Henry De la Beche in his classic *Report on the Geology of Cornwall, Devon & West Somerset* (1839), and use has been made of them in many subsequent works, the most recent being Frank Booker's *Industrial Archaeology of the Tamar Valley*.

After a long period of idleness, activity was resumed throughout the area in the 1780s, mainly through the enterprise of a certain Christopher Gullet of Tavistock. In 1781 Beer [sic] Ferrers Mine[11] was advertising for '20 good lusty hands' and by 1795 it was announced that 76,000 ounces of silver and 1,400 tons of lead ore had been returned from this mine in the previous seven years, realising a sum of £45,000.[12] In 1788 the workings were equipped with a 20in cylinder Boulton & Watt engine which continued in operation until the latter part of

1791 when it was accidentally destroyed by fire. About this time Philip Rashleigh wrote to his fellow Cornish mineralogist, John Hawkins:

> In consequence of your telling me that some Fluors of a different Colour to mine were flung away on the Shammels [stopes] at Beer [*sic*] Alston Mine and that Captain John Vivian knew where to find them, I writ to him desiring he would procure me some. He properly applied to Mr. Gullet for his liberty, who writ me a most impertinent letter on the occasion – on which I shall have no further intercourse with him.[13]

By 1812 the Beer Alston Mine had changed hands, having been taken over by a Mr Smith who formed a company consisting entirely of London shareholders. During June of that year a branch was cut in the bottom level, 5ft wide and 'calculated to produce five tons of rich ore per fathom. Should this continue in length and depth it must prove one of the greatest discoveries ever made in the two counties. We must congratulate Lord Valletort, as heir apparent to the Earl of Mount Edgcumbe (Lord of the soil) who will receive a great increase to his fortune from the dues'.[14]

In 1820 a new merger was formed entitled the Beer Alston Mines comprising the Birch and Cleave Lode (later included in South Tamar Consols), together with the South Hooe Mine. In the former the silver content of the lode varied from 40 to 90oz to the ton of lead, in contrast to South Hooe where it occasionally ran as high as 180oz and the lead (metal) content of the ore averaged 11 to 12 parts in 20. The greatest output of silver in any one year amounted to 3 tons in 1814–15. After that 'too much ore was raised by working the mine too fast – 60 tons of ore per week for a year but a large part of this did not contain more than 40oz per ton of silver'.[15]

The machinery and materials of the Beer Alston Mines as offered for sale in 1821–2 consisted of a 42in cylinder engine on

Boulton & Watt's principle, several horse-whims, a 30ft water-wheel with six heads of stamps, a punching engine, iron pumps, lead moulds, two iron carts, two boats and sails and a barge of 40 tons burthen – 'the whole being conveniently situated for removal from the premises which adjoin the banks of the navigable River Tamar'.[16]

While this might suggest a final closure of the mines, such was far from being the case. In 1835 a new company was formed under the direction of Percival Norton Johnson, celebrated as a metallurgist and assayer and later to establish the well-known firm of Johnson Matthey & Co of Hatton Garden, London. Under the name of the Tamar Silver-Lead Mine, working was resumed at South Hooe (OS Cornwall 38 NW) where in December 1835 Johnson was able to report that the surface works were in a state of 'great forwardness' and the pumping engine ready to go to work in the course of a few weeks. 'I took a sample which after dressing gave 4cwt 2 qrs and 14lbs of lead to the ton which lead produced a proportion of fine silver equal to 113oz to the ton. From my knowledge of these mines when worked in the year 1814 under the name of South Hooe, and calculating the differences in the prices of materials and improvement of machinery at the present time, I have the most sanguine expectations of the undertaking.'[17]

The layout of the workings was peculiar. As the longitudinal section shows, the original shaft was sunk vertically to 226 fathoms, longer and longer levels being required to reach the ore shoot as it pitched south beneath the river. To overcome this in 1843 an incline was started from the 13 fathom level of the vertical shaft and carried down at an angle of 25° to meet the 125 level. Due to the length and weight of the hoisting chain and to facilitate drawing from deeper levels where the ore was still making down, it was decided to sink a perpendicular sub-river shaft, called Spurgin's, from the 115 to the 175 fathoms level. At the top of this shaft a 20hp steam winding and pumping engine was erected – the smoke from the boiler fire being conducted through two miles of old workings before it emerged at surface.

This primitive flue proved not without danger. In 1851 some rich ore was found by tributers in the 95 fathom level through which the flue passed and permission was given to work it, although the men were strictly cautioned by the agents that the place was dangerous because of the smoke. After working for some hours one of the 'pare', feeling unwell, decided to withdraw to the Engine Shaft where, as soon as he had reached a higher level, he fell asleep from the effects of the gas and it was two hours before he reached surface. The others, going out by another way, met the full blast of the smoke which was apparently escaping from a bricked-off level. Four of these men were overcome and died. A fifth was discovered by the rescue party and drawn up in the 'tram' through the incline shaft. After receiving treatment he recovered in due course.[18]

Shortly before this incident an improvement in the ventilation of the deep levels was brought about by the introduction of suction fans. These were at first worked manually and later by a 12ft water-wheel. Prior to this the air was so bad that a candle could scarcely be kept alight for two minutes: 'Now in traversing the levels the miners are compelled to hold their caps before them to prevent them from being blown out', as Johnson reported at the annual meeting of 1845.

In 1850 there were seven steam engines at South Hooe and 200 people were employed. The ores were smelted at Weir Quay in works which had been taken over from an earlier firm. The eighteen furnaces here could smelt over 300 tons of concentrate per month,[19] the normal returns averaging 55 to 60 per cent lead, with a silver content of 60oz to the ton of lead (metal). Occasional parcels ran as high as 145oz.[20]

In 1842 North Hooe (OS Cornwall 38 NW) was reopened under Johnson's direction. Never as rich a mine as South Hooe, it reached its peak in 1846 when a production of 1,200 tons of silver-lead ore was recorded. The shaft was sunk only to

110 fathoms below adit, with levels driven at 10 fathom intervals to the bottom. In the 60 fathom level north the lode was 3ft wide and consisted of fluorspar mixed with silver-lead. The cross-cut at the 110 level was stopped 2 fathoms short of the point where it should have intersected the lode. The mine was reopened in the early part of this century by a small syndicate, but it lacked the necessary capital to lower the water below the 70 fathom level or to carry out any lateral development (Dines, p 682).

By 1854 Johnson had severed his connection with West Country mining and smelting, and the management of the South Hooe Mine was taken over by James Wolferstan. In 1861 the mine was described as the deepest lead mine in England, yet the overall costs of returning 60 tons of ore per month was not more than £800 which left a monthly profit of £300. The richest part of the mine was still in the bottom levels beneath the river bed, and the shallowest level then being worked was the 205.[21] Operations finally ceased about 1885 by which time the workings had reached a depth on the underlie of 250 fathoms below adit.

Ward Mine or more correctly South Ward stands three-quarters of a mile northward of North Hooe, adjacent to the river bank (OS Cornwall 30 SW). A 'puffing' advertisement of this property in *Mining Journal*, 7 November 1835, states that it had been formerly worked for argentiferous lead ore yielding 80 to 190oz of silver to the ton but was discontinued owing to an inundation of the river in which four or five men lost their lives.

The mine was reopened during the summer of 1869 and continued in operation until 1876. The plan as described by Dines shows Engine Shaft sunk vertically to the 60 fathom level and thence on the underlie to the 90. The machinery consisted of a 24in rotary engine for pumping and winding.[22] Recorded production relates only to the years 1873–6 when 130 tons of lead ore and 3900oz of silver were returned. After the abandonment of the mine, the engine-house was converted into a farm-house. The bungalow standing nearby occupies the site of the former count-house.

Of North Ward Mine there is little record, its site being forgotten until 1957 when a subsidence revealed the position of the shaft about 500ft west of North Ward farm.

In a wooded valley on the south bank of the Tamar, south-east of Calstock, Buttspill Mine (OS Cornwall 30 SW) was the most northerly of the mines on the eastern cross-course. The sett is an old one and is said to have been worked in Elizabethan times. It later formed part of the Old Bere group and was worked as such in the opening years of the last century when it was sunk to a depth of 67 fathoms from surface.

Operations were resumed in 1843 when under the name of Green Valley Mine an engine was erected and investigations were carried out in the 17 and 27 fathom levels. Shortly after this the sett was acquired by another small company and re-named Wheal Fancy.

In 1855 the mine was reopened as Berealston United and although work was still entirely confined to the 17 and 27 fathom levels, the returns were sufficiently large to justify the erection of a smelting furnace. During this period attention was chiefly devoted to the reserves of fluorspar which was stated to be of the 'finest quality and could be raised in any quantity at a very low rate'.[23] How long this company survived is not known for certain, but working was resumed on at least two subsequent occasions when the lode was developed to 47 fathoms below adit.

Five shafts are shown on the 1881 edition of the 6in map and the ivy-clad ruins of an engine-house and stack still stand at the southern end of Buttspill Wood. The nearby dump, now much overgrown, is estimated to contain up to 20 per cent of fluorspar. Outputs during the later periods of working are recorded as 95 tons of lead ore, 65oz of silver and 620 tons of fluorspar in 1870-6; and under the name of Tamar (or New Tamar) Valley 90 tons of fluorspar in 1885-6.[24]

In a tributary valley of the Tamar a quarter of a mile east of Buttspill, a north–south lead lode claimed to be rich in silver was opened up in 1846 under the name of Philley Wood or Tuckermarsh Mine.[25] The lode was a recent discovery and by the end of May an adit had been driven some 60 fathoms, gaining 13 fathoms of 'backs' as it entered the rising ground. The lode had an average width of 2ft and a shaft had been started with a view to taking it at 23 fathoms from surface.[26]

Five years later, a prospectus appeared of North Tamar Consols 'formerly Philley Wood or Tuckermarsh Mine'. Reports state that in the previous working the shaft had been sunk to a 10 fathom level below adit from which a few tons of ore were raised. A Mr Evan Hopkins who was called in to advise considered it unlikely that any large bunches of ore would be encountered until the mine had been developed to at least a 30 fathom level: 'the present workings being at too high an elevation to make any great discoveries'. On his recommendation an engine was erected and the shaft deepened to 44 fathoms where three levels were driven north and south. The results, however, were not encouraging, and in 1855 the adventurers decided to abandon the sett and dispose of the machinery which included a new 24in cylinder pumping engine.[27]

About a quarter of a mile from Tuckermarsh Quay lay the Queen of Tamar otherwise known as Great Tamar, by which latter name it is shown on C. Williams's *Map of the Tavistock Mining District* (1859). A brief notice in *Mining Journal* on 9 July of that year states that the workings were only 4 fathoms deep but had produced an abundance of highly mineralised gossan from an east–west lode. The mine is not mentioned by Dines but is said by Collins to have returned both lead and copper ores.

It is possible that the same lode may have been worked in Wheal Jenny a short distance south-east of Tuckermarsh hamlet where its site is marked on the 6in map, Cornwall 30 SW.

Nothing is known of its early history and most of the surface features are thought to have been obliterated when the nearby railway embankment was made. The mine is said to have been last tried in 1915 when a small portable engine was erected on the shaft. In clearing this it was found that the old men had removed all the lead ore in sight and no fresh development was carried out.[28]

From Buttspill southwards the eastern cross-course was developed on the mines of Lockridge (otherwise Goldstreet), Furzehill (or Whitsam Down), East Tamar and South Tamar (OS Cornwall 38 NW). Early in the 1840s the latter two were worked in concert by the Berealston Mining Company and created extraordinary excitement:

> Vast quantities of silver were brought to London and, on occasions, the whole mail was engaged to carry it. The establishment in London consisted of seven directors with large salaries – in addition to two managing directors at the mines. The offices in Bishopsgate Street were like a palace and an usher with a gold stick stood at the door. That the company soon failed is not to be wondered at.[29]

A fresh start was made in 1845 when Whitsam, Lockridge and Furzehill were amalgamated under the name of East Tamar Consols. By 1847 six shafts had been cleared to depths of 30 to 40 fathoms below adit – the latter being 30 fathoms from surface in the higher part of the sett. At Whitsam (the southern portion of Lockridge) the shaft was deepened from 46 to 60 fathoms under adit, the water being drawn by a 40in cylinder engine. Five ends were then driving, all in productive ground. At Lockridge (identifiable by its tall and unusually ornamented chimney-stack) the shaft was 50 fathoms deep and was shortly after sunk to 54 fathoms in order to connect with a level then heading towards it from Whitsam. At Furzehill the shaft had been sunk from 30 to 46 fathoms and had four ends driving, all showing good values. The bottom level, south, was about to come in under the 'former Charlotte and Caroline Shafts'. The matrix of the lode consisted of fluorspar which then realised 10s a ton. The mine was equipped with a 58in cylinder pumping engine and a 36in winding and stamping engine, operating 24 heads of stamps and a crusher. Ores to the value of £10,000 had been sold.

During the commercial crisis of 1847, the holders of a majority of the shares became bankrupt. The mines, however, were taken over by a new company in April 1848, with James Wolferstan acting as general manager. By the spring of 1849 production was averaging 30 tons a month which was about paying costs. Five years later it was reported that the Furzehill Engine Shaft had been sunk below the 112 fathom level, and by 1861 the East Tamar group as a whole had returned 2,580 tons of lead ore, 19,530 ounces of silver and over 1,400 tons of fluorspar.[30]

South Tamar Consols (OS Cornwall 38 NW), the southern-most mine of the eastern cross-course, has been worked on a number of occasions, although little is known of its early history other than the tradition that it had returned large quantities of ore before 1817.

Operations were renewed in 1846 and with one short period of suspension continued for the next ten years. By May 1847 the rehabilitation of the mine was well under way, the adit had been cleared for nearly 300 fathoms and a 6oin engine was being erected on Cowie's Shaft,[31] then 90 fathoms deep, adjacent to the river. First sales of ore were recorded in August 1849 and a year later the mine was making a small monthly profit and was 124 fathoms deep.[32] Engine Shaft was eventually carried down to 148 fathoms on the underlie, although no stoping was done below the 136. The deeper levels in the southern part of the mine extended fully half a mile out beneath the waters of the Tamar.

As in the case of other leading West Country mines, South Tamar was visited by a number of distinguished tourists. On

44

3 August 1850 *Mining Journal* recorded the arrival a few days previously of His Highness the Nepalese Ambassador and his suite. Accompanied up-river by naval officers from Plymouth, the party landed at Millshead midway between the mine and Weir Quay. After inspecting the machinery and surface operations, the ambassador and three of his suite proceeded underground. Descending Glynn's Shaft, the party passed through the 90 fathom level and thence down the Engine Shaft to the 100. While going through this level, the ambassador frequently exclaimed 'Beautiful, beautiful' as he admired the lode in the back, being no less struck with the power of the engine which drained the water from this level, 600ft below the river bed. The rapidity with which his highness descended the ladders, climbed into the stopes and came to surface again astonished all who were present. After changing out of his underground clothes he sat in front of the account-house and partook of a basket of cherries, being the only kind of refreshment of which he might partake, presented to him by Miss Jackson who resided near the mine. For this the lady was liberally rewarded, as was also Captain Tremayne, the agent, who had accompanied him underground. On his departure from the mine which was not until 8 pm, he presented his 'sol-umbra' (sunshade) to Mr James Wolferstan, the manager.

During 1851 the monthly output of ore rose from 45 tons in March to 80 tons in December. At the end of this year reserves were about 663 tons, enough for eight and a half months. Three years later most of the development points were still looking well. The lode in the 136 fathom level, south, was yielding 9cwt of ore per fathom, and in the end of the 124 level the yield was 15cwt. Two stopes in the back of the 112 were producing 30cwt and 25cwt respectively. In the previous month the lode in the 100 end had averaged 2 tons of ore per fathom. Somewhat lesser values were being obtained in the 80, 70, 60, 40 and 30 fathom levels, all of which, however, were being stoped at a profit. Mankin's Shaft had recently been cleared to the bottom or 90 fathom level. Some very good ore ground was standing here, but the air being bad, a winze was being sunk from the 80 level in order to improve the ventilation in this part of the mine.[33]

In the summer of 1856 a total of 144 men were employed underground and 130 men, women and children at surface; whilst returns were averaging a regular 100 tons of lead ore per month. Six weeks later came disaster. At about 8 pm on 31 August 1856, the waters of the Tamar broke into the mine, completely flooding the workings. Providentially this occurred on a Sunday when there was no one underground; had it been twelve hours later some ninety-five men and boys must in all probability have lost their lives. The inrush took place through a clay-filled slide or fault about halfway out under the river, and, according to eye-witnesses, such was the force of the pent-up air as it was expelled from the workings that it burst off the capping of the disused shafts with a report resembling thunder.

The existence of the slide was, of course, well known but so little apprehension had it ever caused that a number of levels had been driven through and beyond it. At a special meeting of the company held in London on the Thursday following, the manager reported that at the time of the disaster the prospects were excellent: 'they were looking better at every point'. The richest portion of the lode lay beneath the centre of the river, where a considerable tonnage of ore was lying broken in the levels waiting to be brought to surface. Despite this he did not consider there was any hope of recovering the mine. The breach might be sealed and the water pumped out but this would take two years to complete, with an expenditure of 4,000 tons of coal, and even then the water would probably find its way in again.

However, the matter did not rest there and for weeks after the correspondence columns of *Mining Journal* were filled with suggestions for salvaging the mine. A committee was appointed consisting of leading engineers, mineral agents and practical timbermen to investigate these schemes but eventually reported that none appeared practicable. It was accordingly resolved to wind up the company and realise the assets, the whole of the machinery including five steam engines being offered for sale in Plymouth in December of that year. Today a solitary stack remains as a monument to this once-celebrated mine – one of the very few on record to be abandoned when still in full production.

East of the Tamar, the River Tavy follows a serpentine but roughly parallel course southwards, eventually uniting with its greater sister a little below Bere Ferrers. The mines of Tavy conform to the size of the valley through which it flows. More intimate in character and worked on a smaller scale than those of the Tamar, they are approachable for the most part only by steep and rugged woodland tracks and due to their seclusion are comparatively little known.

At Double Waters, near the confluence of the Tavy and the Walkham rivers the celebrated Virtuous Lady Mine (OS 111 NE) stands in a lovely setting of woodlands interspersed with outcrops of fern-covered rock. The mine is undoubtedly of great antiquity deriving its name, as is generally supposed, from Elizabeth I. The ore occurs in beds bearing east–west, slightly underlaying north and varying in width from a few inches to 20 or 30ft.[34] These have been exploited for 100 fathoms along the strike and 120 fathoms down the dip, the deepest workings being little more than 20 fathoms below river (Dines, p 700).

The mine was visited by Henrik Kahlmeter in November 1724 who noted that the vein then being worked 'was 8ft and is now 10ft broad'. The mineral owner was named Dean, the principal lessees being the Bristol [Copper] Company. Production at that time amounted to 9 or 10 tons of 'clean ore' in three months, the miners receiving £3 10s per ton and providing their own tools. At the most recent sale the ore fetched £4 10s per ton which Kahlmeter was informed would yield one ton of copper (metal). From this he estimated the quantity of fine copper in the ore to be 16 per cent.

The mine has been worked on many subsequent occasions. In 1849 it was stated that the 'late company' was very successful in its operations and that a Captain Williams, who held a large interest in the concern, had realised a fortune in a few years. About 1841, however, the lode had been lost and thereafter production ceased for six or seven years. Working was resumed in 1848 when in driving a cross-cut from the 24 fathom level a lode of great size was cut from which 50 tons of copper ore was sold in two months. A short time after another parcel of 54 tons was dispatched to Messrs Vivian & Son, the Swansea smelters, whilst a further 50 tons was expected to be ready for sale in January 1850, the produce varying from 6 to 8 per cent copper.[35] The mine at this period was known as Virtuous Lady and Bedford since due to its northward dip the ore-body was then being developed on the further side of the Tavy in a sett named Wheal Bedford. Here it was opened up by at least three shafts sunk near the river bank.

In December 1857 tributers searching in the side of one of the subterranean caverns excavated by former workers, cut into a new 'flat' or bed yielding more than 4 tons of ore per fathom. This discovery was made at only 15 fathoms from surface and was in 'whole' (unworked) ground. At these shallow depths 'vughs' or natural hollows in the rock were frequently lined with colourful specimens in great variety:

> Brilliant, well defined crystals of titanium, fishscale iron, milk and cream quartz, tetrahedral crystals of copper, red, blue, purple, yellow and violet . . . which when turned about under the rays of the sun reflect a different colour from every different angle of incidence – orange, gold, crimson, violet and green

as a local mineralogist[36] described them in 1835. Latterly the mine was worked almost solely for the value of such specimens, the men laying trusses of straw on the floor of the workings to prevent their being damaged as they were detached from the rock.[37] Throughout its history, the Virtuous Lady has always been something of a show place, as indeed it still is, although many of the caverns which inspired the Victorian sightseer with 'fearsome awe' are no longer accessible today.

Downstream from Virtuous Lady, the Tavy passes some half-dozen other mines in its meandering course. In Blackmoorham Wood the lodes of Little Duke, otherwise known as North Tavy or Raven Rock (OS 111 NE), are thought to be a continuation of those worked in Bedford Consols in Maddacleave Wood on the Tamar. The mine was developed largely by adits, Deep Adit driven west from the river bank being 50 fathoms below surface on the high ground near the railway track. Near this three underlay shafts exploited the shallower parts of the lodes. Worked in its earlier days for copper ore, of which it returned some 40 tons in 1824, the mine was restarted in 1845 when it was said that £14,000 had formerly been expended and the mine as a consequence was 'very much opened'.[38] Production at this period was obtained chiefly from the 20 and 30 fathom levels where the main lode averaged 10 to 12ft in width.

The mine was again active in 1859 when as Raven Rock (formerly North Tavy) it was claimed to possess in addition to copper a large extent of tin ground standing above the 30 fathom level. In six weeks four men and four boys had raised about 2 tons of tin stuff which left a satisfactory profit for their labour.[39]

Reopened in 1907 for tin and arsenic, good values were encountered in the western part of the mine. In later years, however, little work was done below the 20 fathom level and the Deep Adit was not cleared.

At one period Buller and Bertha Mine was included in this last sett. The former lies nearly a mile to the east and is marked by a large slaty burrow standing between the plantations of Hele and Alston (OS 111 NE). Little is known of this mine

49

which ceased operations in 1855 (although working resumed for a short period in 1861). Near the shaft are the remains of a count-house or possibly the miners' dry.

Hocklake Mine, a third of a mile south of Little Duke, had been started before November 1724, when it was visited by Henrik Kahlmeter on his way to Cornwall. He described the sett as being in two parts, a lower working called The Duke and an upper portion named Stocklake – both under grant to the Bristol Company from 'one Dodche [?] who receives ⅛ dues'. Drained by an adit at the foot of the hill, the Duke Lode was 6 to 10ft wide and had been developed to a depth of 14 fathoms. In the course of the previous summer 16½ tons of copper ore had been sold at £4 per ton, and they were expecting to produce another 8 tons before Christmas. Five men were then employed on tribute.

During the last century, under the name of Tavy Consols, the mine was developed to a depth of 90 fathoms below adit on the underlie and continued to be worked intermittently until 1891. The machinery consisted of a 40ft wheel for pumping and another of 30ft diameter for crushing and winding, water to drive these being brought by a continuation of the leat from Virtuous Lady Mine. The lodes were exceptionally rich in arsenical ore, the calciners on the mine commonly 'burning' 125 tons a month, with a monthly output of 15 tons of refined arsenic.[40] The ruined furnaces, still to be seen in 1958, are now largely destroyed; the chimney-stack (OS 111 NE) was demolished in 1928.

Lady Bertha on the east bank of the river had the same lodes as those of Tavy Consols and was started as a 'new mine' in 1855. In the first six months of working, 86 tons of copper ore were returned from a depth of only 15 fathoms, a fact which caused a fever of excitement in the volatile mining circles of Tavistock. During the succeeding years four shafts were sunk at Meadow, Engine, Moyle's and Eastern, the last being vertical to a 53 fathom level. The mine was worked solely by water-power, the water being conveyed through a leat three miles in length from a point on the Walkham River above Grenofen Bridge, giving a fall at the mine of nearly 180ft. A large wheel situated between the Engine and Eastern Shafts pumped from both. The water then flowed through a lobby to a second wheel which served for hoisting at Engine Shaft. Below this a third wheel operated the grinders, jigs and stamps whilst, lower down, a fourth wheel hauled the tailings up to the waste dumps.

The arsenical pyrites, of which the mine produced great quantities, was carried across the river by a suspension bridge[41] to the calciners at Tavy Consols. Here it was burnt for arsenic, the rinkle (burnt residues) being then trammed back to Lady Bertha where it was stamped and treated for tin. There were fifteen heads of stamps on the mine, five of which worked by day and ten by night (when the rolls were stopped).[42] Due to the prevailing depression in mining and the low price of arsenic, operations ceased towards the end of 1868; £35,000 worth of copper ore having been sold during this working in addition to small quantities of tin.

Operations were resumed in 1880 when a 45ft wheel was installed, with a line of flat-rods connecting to the pit-work in the shaft. On 25 November the water was turned on and 'as the massive wheel moved round for the first time, Mr Sharpe, one of the directors, dashed a bottle of champagne against it and christened it Wheal Emily'. Preparations were then being made to erect another wheel, 30ft by 4ft, to work a double-acting haulage engine, in addition to crushers. Both wheels had been manufactured by Messrs James and H. Pearce of Tavistock, under the superintendence of Matthew Loam, the engineer of the mine.[43]

During this working, which continued until 1891, fresh development was carried out both laterally and in depth. A hitherto unpublished report, dated 6 March 1895, by William Henry Clemo of Devon Great Consols shows that

Eastern Shaft had been deepened prior to this time to 77 fathoms. Here a level had been driven 13 fathoms east on a lode 3ft in width, yielding 2 tons of arsenical ore per fathom. The same level extended 18 fathoms west where the values were similar and the lode was 4½ft wide. At the 65 east the level reached a cross-course and had been stoped in the back and bottom, producing 8 tons of mundic per fathom over a width of 5ft. Westwards the lode was 4ft wide and promising. In the 53 level east the lode had a width of 6ft and yielded 3 tons of ore per fathom. Stoping in the bottom produced 6 tons of pyrite and 2 tons of copper ore per fathom. From Western Shaft the 41, 30 and 20 fathom levels showed lode widths varying from 2½ to 5ft, stoping in the backs and bottoms yielding 4, 6 and 3 tons of ore per fathom. At the then ruling price of arsenic, the writer considered that there was a fair prospect of the mine being worked again at a profit.[44]

During the working of 1880 to 1891, the directors of Lady Bertha acquired the sett of East Lady Bertha into which the lodes of the former were believed to run. East Bertha Shaft was in course of sinking in 1860 when it reached a depth of 29 fathoms and was equipped with a 14in horizontal engine adapted for pumping and winding.[45] No plans are known of this mine, which Dines dismisses as little more than a trial. The size of the dump, however, suggests that fairly considerable development must have been carried out. The chimney-stack shown on the 1906 edition of the OS map (111 NE) has since been demolished.

About half a mile downstream on the east bank of the river South Lady Bertha, otherwise known as Ludbrook Mine, had three lodes, with a shaft sunk vertically to 40 fathoms from which levels were extended eastwards at 40, 30 and 20 fathoms. The mine is known to have been in operation in 1857 and despite Dines's statement that there are no records of output, there is evidence to show that 147 tons of copper ore were sold in the years 1859–61,[46] but working ceased soon after the latter date.

Page 53
(*above*) Gawton Mine, showing engine-house and adjoining grinding-houses; (*below*) an earlier view from Rumleigh works shows clearly the line of the arsenic flues of Gawton Mine and their harmful effect on vegetation. The dumps in the left foreground are those of Okel Tor Mine on the Cornish bank of the River Tamar

The mine now lies in the garden of a private house and the remaining dumps are much overgrown.

Immediately opposite South Lady Bertha an old shaft situated near the west bank of the river marks the site of Denham Bridge Mine. According to *Mining Journal*, 20 November 1858, two copper lodes discovered here in a former working were partially explored by driving adits at river level. North Lode was thought to be an extension of the one then being worked in South Lady Bertha. From the Denham Bridge South Lode, £700 to £800 worth of ore was obtained by stoping the back of the adit for a short distance. A new company was formed soon after this, 7 tons of copper ore being sold for £13 in 1860.[47]

Output from Lady Bertha, Tavy Consols and other mines of this area was carried to the Tamar for shipment, principally from Gawton Quay which was the nearest point on the river. The journey was performed in two stages, pack animals being used to transport the ore up the steeply wooded slopes of the Tavy. At Tavisock Cross, on the Rock to Bere Alston road, midway between the two rivers, the ore was deposited on a stockpile; a cottage standing here bearing the name Orestock was formerly occupied by a caretaker who supervised the transfer of the ore to horse-drawn wagons which completed its transit to the Tamar.

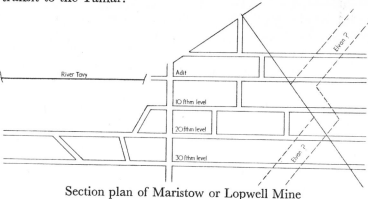

Section plan of Maristow or Lopwell Mine

Near the mouth of the Tavy, two or more lead lodes extend northwards along the west bank of the river for fully a mile. These have been developed at their southern end in Wheal Maristow (or the Lopwell Mine) and further north in the Wood Mine (OS 111 SE). Operations at the former are believed to have been started early in the last century when a shaft was sunk and a Cornish pumping engine erected, the ruined engine-house of which still remains. To conform with terms imposed by the mineral owner, Sir Massey Lopes, a flue was constructed 400yd in length to the summit of Whitacliffe Wood where the stack was erected out of sight of Maristow House. The dressing-floors lay a short distance upstream and near this there was a small lead smelter. No trace of the latter now remains, beyond a few large blocks of granite, whilst the engine-house stack has also been demolished, although both were remembered by old people recently living in the neighbourhood.

A plan of the mine dated 1822, in the Maristow Estate Office, shows that Engine Shaft was sunk to 40 fathoms at which depth levels were driven 30 fathoms north and 100 fathoms south. According to local tradition, the most productive part of the lode extended further south beneath the river into Maristow Park, where the miners used to boast that they would one day 'hole through' to the squire's wine cellar. On this becoming known to Sir Massey, he was so much incensed that he sent his estate carpenter over to the mine with orders to cut the main rod of the engine. The truth of this story was confirmed in 1952 by the late R. W. Toll who, on examining the shaft, noted that the rod had in fact been cut off about a foot above water level. It was subsequently learnt that there are letters in existence in the Maristow Office relating to an encroachment under the park at about this time.[48]

North of the Maristow Mine, old workings and shallow gunnises can be traced continuously to the Wood Mine in Great Whiterock Wood, a distance of one mile. Work was resumed at the Wood Mine in 1851 when an adit was cleared for 400 fathoms, passing through several shafts. In one of these the lode at a depth of 32 fathoms showed values of 10½oz of silver to the ton of lead ore, whilst in White Rock Shaft the lode was 15in wide and producing fine stones of gossan. Among other shafts which were cleared Middle Shaft and South Shaft proved to be 45 and 32 fathoms deep from surface respectively. Captain Charles Thomas, who inspected the property at this time, reported that for 30 fathoms north of Middle Shaft and 20 fathoms south the back of the adit had been entirely stoped away by former workers. In the end going south the lode contained a little lead but elsewhere appeared almost worthless. Near White Rock Shaft a small dump showed some small strings of nearly pure galena. Because of the depth of the water it was impossible to examine the lodes below the adit level.[49] By 1855 the mine was at a low ebb financially, the majority of the adventurers being in default on their 'calls'. It was nevertheless agreed to give the property a further period of trial. On the advice of the agents it was decided to abandon White Rock Shaft and to enlarge Middle Shaft, subsequently attaching flat-rods to the engine in order to sink it 20 fathoms below the adit. At the same time, instructions were given that the cylinder, which had been installed without any 'clothing', should be properly lagged in order to effect a saving in fuel.[50]

The shares continued to be listed in the *Mining Journal* until the end of 1857, by which date operations had ceased. Sales of 4 tons of ore are recorded in Hunt's *Mineral Statistics* for 1852 and a further 8 tons were sold in 1856. Other sales are believed to have been made by private contract.

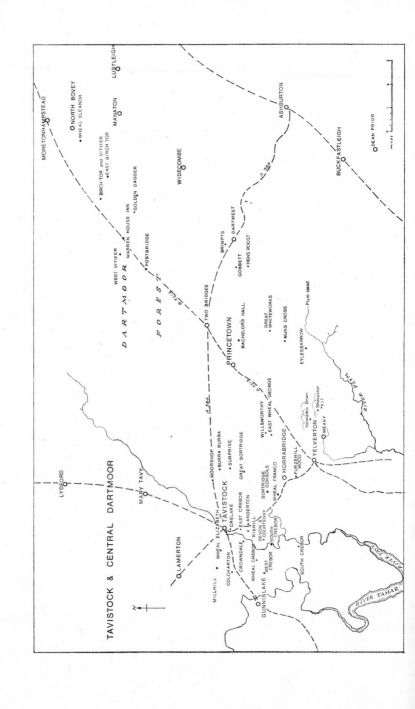

TAVISTOCK & CENTRAL DARTMOOR

LUSTLEIGH

MORETONHAMPSTEAD

○ NORTH BOVEY
• WHEAL ELEANOR

MANATON

ASHBURTON

BIRCH TOR and VITIFER
• EAST BIRCH TOR

BUCKFASTLEIGH

WIDECOMBE

○ DEAN PRIOR

D A R T M O O R

WEST VITIFER
WARREN HOUSE INN
• GOLDEN DAGGER

• POSTBRIDGE

F O R E S T

BRIMPTS
DARTMEET

GOBBETT
• HENS ROOST

TWO BRIDGES

PRINCETOWN
• BACHELOR'S HALL

GREAT
• WHITEWORKS
• NUNS CROSS

Plym Head

EYLESBARROW

LYDFORD

MOORSHOP
BURRA BURRA
• SURPRISE

WILLSWORTHY
EAST WHEAL GEORGE

MARY TAVY

GREAT SORTRIDGE

Yennadon Down
Sheepstor
• KIT

MEAVY

MILLHILL

• WHEAL ELIZABETH
TAVISTOCK
• CRELAKE

SORTRIDGE
CONSOLS
WHEAL FRANCO

HORRABRIDGE
FURZEHILL
WOOD

YELVERTON

COLCHARTON
CROWNDALE

EAST CREBOR
LANDERTON
DEVON &
COURTENAY

LAMERTON

WHEAL CREBOR
RIXHILL
WEST
CREBOR
SOUTH
CREBOR

GUNNISLAKE

SOUTH CREBOR

WEST RIVER

RIVER TAMAR

N

PART TWO

AROUND TAVISTOCK

During the years when Devon Great Consols was rising to its
zenith, a number of trials were made in the hope of finding an
extension of its phenomenally rich lodes to the east. In 1845
prospecting started on the Crease estate to the east of Millhill
in the Lumburn Valley (OS 105 NE). Under the title of Wheal
Elizabeth (late Crease) the sett was claimed to have three lodes
varying in width from 2 to 10ft and likely to form a junction
in depth. On one of these a shaft was sunk to 17 fathoms from
which short cross-cuts were driven south in search of the Wheal
Maria lode. At a depth of 4 fathoms from surface a copper lode
was intersected which produced some good yellow ore. The
workings, however, were only trifling in extent and carried on
with 'little spirit'. Operations continued intermittently for
about two years after which the search was abandoned.

Undaunted by this, the sett was taken up again in 1848,
being then known as East Wheal Josiah. In driving the deep
adit, a new lode was discovered producing good stones of
gossan and mundic 'precisely of the same sort as that found
in the Maria and Wheal Josiah mines of Devon Great Consols'.
The workings on this lode, however, were little more than 36ft
below surface; although stones of 'beautiful' yellow copper ore
were encountered, the trial proved no more successful than
those which had preceded it.[1]

In the 1860s more vigorous efforts were made by the East
Devon Great Consols company. Three east–west lodes were
opened up, two of which, underlying north, were expected to

59

form a junction with the Devon Great Consols Lode which underlay south. In the following year work was in progress on the middle lode where an engine shaft was sunk to an ultimate depth of 70 fathoms. On this a small high-pressure puffer-engine was erected with two 9in cylinders. Some 80 fathoms south another shaft was sunk to 18 fathoms on a lead-bearing cross-course. In 1862 the mine employed eighteen people and a cross-cut was being driven from the 70 fathom level towards a copper lode which had earlier been seen in the 40 level. Although said to be producing lead and copper ores at this time, no sales appear to have been recorded. In November 1864 an unfavourable report was received from the manager and in the following month it was resolved to abandon the mine 'as it does not hold out prospects that would warrant its continuation'. The site of the engine shaft is probably identifiable with a large slatey burrow on the north side of the byroad leading from Middle Lumburn Bridge to Tavistock – nearly opposite the entrance to Crease farm house[2] (OS 105 NE).

Colcharton Mine (OS 105 SE), otherwise Devon and Bedford, lay a short distance west of Lumburn. Although making no claims to possess the Devon Great Consols lodes, it was worked on a fairly considerable scale. In 1863 it was equipped with a 30in rotary engine which served for pumping, hoisting and crushing. From the vertical shaft, cross-cuts were put out at depths of 20, 30 and 40 fathoms and levels extended west on the lode to a maximum length of 115 fathoms. By 1867 no returns had been made, but twelve men were still employed in sinking the shaft, which eventually reached a 65 fathom level from surface. Soon after this the pumps were withdrawn, the outlook for the mine being considered unfavourable.[3]

Shortly after the commencement of work at the northern end of the Tavistock Canal tunnel in 1803, a copper lode showing good values was encountered close to the mouth. To develop this a mining company was formed entitled Wheal Crebor, a name derived from the adjoining farm (OS 105 SE). Further discoveries made in February and March 1805 resulted in the sale of 20 tons of ore. By 1807 the adit, which was driven beneath the floor of the canal, had been extended for more than 200 fathoms on Middle Lode and was then carried across to North Lode on which it was continued. In August 1808, Engine Shaft was down to a 12 fathom level, Cock's Shaft and Smith's Shaft had been sunk to 24 and 12 fathoms respectively, and Kelly's Shaft to adit. The outlay on the mine by this date amounted to £5,007 as against sales of only £163.

After this conditions improved rapidly. In 1811 output was averaging 150 tons a quarter, and by the following year had increased to 155 tons a month. With the price of copper falling due to (temporary) over-production, news such as this was far from welcome to the mining interests of West Cornwall. 'On the western edge of Devonshire,' wrote William Jenkin from Redruth in October 1812, 'the Canal Company have discovered (in cutting through a hill) a large Copper Lode. What will become of *this* poor County!' Crebor was losing money in that year but in 1813 showed a profit of £5,462 and paid a dividend of £15 a share.

Total costs to this date amounted to £33,449 with a net return of £32,098. About this time, rich ore was being obtained from the Georgina Lode which was intersected by the tunnel between a third and half a mile from its entrance. This lode was developed solely within the tunnel, ore from the stopes being let down through box-holes into barges drawn up to receive it. In the year ended November 1814, 3,648 tons of ore were sold at a profit of £7,000, and two dividends were paid totalling £45 per share.

The mine was abandoned in 1828 when the owner of adjoining land to the west refused to grant an extension of the sett. By that time Cock's, Smith's, Kelly's and Rundle's Shafts had been sunk to 45, 100, 135 and 104 fathoms from surface respectively, while sales of ore totalling 27,490 tons had realised £167,181. In 1844 a new company was formed, but shortly afterwards failed in the railway panic and financial depression of 1846.[4]

Working was resumed in 1851 and continued for the next fifty years, 34,900 tons of copper ore being returned between 1852 and 1893, together with considerable quantities of pyrite and mispickel during the years 1872 to 1901. The mine lasted so long mainly because of the advantages of cheap transport (the direct connection with the quays of Morwellham saving it the cost of land carriage which had crippled other mines of this district) and power which it gained from being on the canal.

Drainage was also effected by the flow of water through the canal. A 40ft wheel, 8ft breast, erected near the northern entrance of the tunnel, operated a line of flat-rods 3,000ft in length, extending up an incline to the top of the hill where by means of a T-bob it connected to the pumps in Rundle's Shaft, the most westerly on the property. Another wheel of 16ft diameter, similarly driven by the canal, drove a crusher. The only steam engine on the mine was a 22in rotary which served for hoisting, supplementing the work of the numerous horse-whims.

In 1889 a crisis arose. Due in part to a recent fall of £40 a ton in the price of copper and still more to the near exhaustion of the lodes, the mine was faced with the prospect of immediate closure. At this juncture Moses Bawden, then acting manager, came forward with an offer to lease the mine for a period of twelve months, paying the company a tribute of 2s 6d in the £ on the ores sold. As he remarked at the meeting 'We have worked the mine boldly and sunk it from the 156 to the 200 purely on speculation, though each level has proved very poor. Nevertheless, if I had the working of the mine myself, instead of stopping at the 200, I would sink another 40 fathoms. I cannot believe that the tremendous courses of ore we had from the 108 to the 144 have entirely died out.'[5] After some discussion, Mr Bawden's offer was accepted, and although the mine was never deepened below the 200, the demand for arsenic enabled it to survive until 1901, the year which also witnessed the demise of its celebrated neighbour, Devon Great Consols.

As was the case with other well-known mines, Wheal Crebor fathered a considerable progeny. Best known of these was West Crebor (OS 105 SE) whose engine-house, with a detached stack, until recently formed a conspicuous landmark on the high plateau of Morwell Down. The sett is separated from Wheal Crebor by 170 fathoms of ground and was connected to the workings of the latter at adit level only. Started in the 1880s, West Crebor was developed to a 60 fathom level on the underlie of the lode but without much success, the sole output recorded being 19 tons of copper ore in 1885.[6]

North Crebor produced 916 tons of copper ore between 1829 and 1835 but is otherwise unknown. Dines thought that it formed part of Crelake, a mine which in fact was not started until twenty years later. A more probable identification is that of a shaft (now obliterated but shown on the 1882 edition of the OS map 105 SE) which lay at the loop of the road, near the second milestone from Tavistock, 200yd north of the Harvest Home inn.

Information regarding South Crebor Mine is principally derived from a report made by C. F. Barclay and R. W. Toll[7] who worked it for a short period in the winter of 1922–3. Little is known of its early history, but the adit is said to have been started between 1830 and 1840 and was eventually driven 360 fathoms from its portal, 610yd south of Shilla Mill Bridge. About 1860 the sett was taken up by a Captain Goldsworthy, previously manager of East Wheal Russell, and continued intermittently to be worked by him until 1870 or 1880, sometimes with assistance from the adventurers of Wheal Crebor. A vertical shaft was sunk 24 fathoms from surface and at that depth a cross-cut was driven north to the lode, on which a level extended a considerable distance east and west. The lode was very bunchy and had been worked mainly by tributers.

The mine is situated in the steeply sided valley of the Tavy immediately north of Lazy Bench Hill Bridge where it spans the now-disused railway. An engine-house is shown here on the 1882 edition of the OS map 105 SE. According to Barclay and Toll, the Engine Shaft 'on top of the higher dump' is vertical to 44 fathoms from surface, but being sollared over is not easily visible, a fact which no doubt accounts for its not being marked on the map. The mine's sole recorded production is stated as 226 tons of copper ore in the years 1863–7, a figure which is probably incomplete.

On the west side of the valley the South Crebor lodes have been prospected in New East Russell, a small mine which owed its inception to the erstwhile reputation of East Wheal Russell further to the west. In 1868 the deepest level in New East Russell was 20 fathoms below adit (40 fathoms), few men were employed and the only 'machinery' consisted of a horse-whim. Working ceased in that year with a recorded output of 67 tons of copper ore in 1865. Working was resumed in 1870 under the name of Wheal Courtenay[8] but no further development appears to have been carried out either laterally or in depth.

On the east side of the Tavy, the same lodes were explored by an adit beneath Birch Wood into the sett of Devon and Courtenay (OS 105 SE) which was developed to a 90 fathom level from surface. From the 30 level downwards the plans show a number of small stopes, but according to Dines less than 15 per cent of the blocked-out ground has been removed. In 1861 the mine was employing fifty people[9] but ceased work soon after, with an output in 1852 of 1,510 tons of copper ore and 3 tons of lead ore. The burrows of the principal shaft adjacent to Middle Tor farm contain quantities of iron pyrites, together with purple fluorspar.

A mile south of Tavistock, Crowndale Mine (OS 105 SE), whose overgrown workings adjoin the former railway, developed an eastward extension of the Crebor main lode. The mine is an old one, resuscitated in 1799 when its machinery consisted mainly of water-wheels. These were originally driven by a leat from the Tavy and later by the flow of water through the Tavistock Canal. An old plan of the mine shows no less than eighteen shafts over a length of 500 fathoms, the deepest being sunk vertically to a 90 fathom level. The most productive part of the lode lay above the 40 fathom level – below this the values declined.[10]

During the 1830s the Tavistock Smelting Company established works on the sett, treating ores from the waste dumps of the surrounding mines, together with partially smelted residues known as Jews' tin from the ancient blowing-houses on Dartmoor.[11] The mine continued to be worked at intervals until the 1870s, returning over 15,000 tons of copper ore, principally in the period between 1820 and 1830.

In 1924–6 the adit was reopened for arsenic when an ore shoot was found averaging $4\frac{1}{2}$ft in width and estimated to contain from 10,000 to 15,000 tons. Samples of copper pyrites assayed 4dwts of gold per ton.[12]

The Crowndale main lode crosses the Tavy south of Crowndale farm where it enters the sett of East Crebor (OS 105 SE). Although a comparatively small mine, the latter is said to have produced some of the richest ore ever found in Cornwall or Devon, assaying 28 per cent copper.[13] In July 1880 three men were drowned in the 70 fathom level by an influx of the Tavy through the adit, the water at the same time flooding part of the Crowndale workings. The engine shaft of that mine still registers the rise and fall of the river.[14] An undated plan of East Crebor shows two lodes, 15 fathoms apart, between which the shaft was sunk vertically to 70 fathoms below adit. Part of the engine-house, converted to a barn, was still standing here in 1958.

East Crebor had been worked at an earlier period as East Crowndale. In 1811 the latter was described as being in its infancy but had already sold ores to the value of £6,277.[15] In the same year an output of 1,775 tons was recorded under the name of South Crowndale which so nearly adjoined East Crowndale as to constitute virtually one sett. Work was in progress at both mines in the middle of the last century, East Crowndale selling 605 tons of ore in the years 1852–4.[16] The machinery at this time included a 56in pumping and a 26in winding and stamps engine. South Crowndale, which was also known as West Rix Hill, was active again in 1858 when two new lodes standing 10–12 fathoms apart were discovered by surface pitting.[17]

Adjoining the above group on the east lie Rix Hill, New Anderton and Old Anderton, the two latter situated on the slopes of the Tiddy Brook (OS 105 SE). Wheal Anderton had been sunk to an 80 fathom level by 1849 and was subsequently deepened to the 90. Shortly before that time Wheal Ash was added to the sett, and the mines became known as Tavistock Consols. On the Wheal Ash Lode, the adit passed through an immense course of mundic, nearly solid, and extending for a length of 60 fathoms.

In 1850 arrangements were made for combining Wheals Anderton and Ash under the title of Tavistock United Mines. Rix Hill was not included in this lease, but was working independently for tin on which it was said to be making considerable profits.[18]

In 1880 a fresh amalgamation was proposed comprising the two Andertons and the Rix Hill mines under the old name of East Crowndale. The sett thus formed incorporated three east–west tin lodes, with a number of copper lodes running parallel – the latter 'extending through East Crebor, being a continuation of those extensively worked in the Old Crowndale Mine'. Five shafts had already been sunk on the Anderton and Rix Hill properties where the lodes were reported to contain between 150lb and 5cwt of tin to the ton of stuff.[19] Whether the new company ever materialised is doubtful, since no other reference to East Crowndale has been found at this period. The constituent mines, however, continued to work until 1890 returning, in the aggregate, a considerable quantity of tin for which their potential is thought to be not yet exhausted.

In the built-up area on the south side of Tavistock, a sett named Wheal Pixon was granted in 1834 to John Gill and John Rundle, comprising the farms of Fitzford and Beercause, with 200 fathoms on the course of the lode, east and west of Ford Street turnpike gatehouse. To this was added a length of ground north and south of the point where the Wheal Crowndale cross-course was supposed to intersect the Wheal Pixon Lode.[20] In 1838, twenty-seven people were employed on the mine of which little else is known.

Crelake Mine (OS 105 SE), closely adjoining Wheal Pixon, was started in 1857 when a copper lode was discovered in the bed of the nearby Tavy. The sett as originally granted to Richard Davey MP 'and other influential gentlemen of West Cornwall',[21] extended one mile east from the river and contained two east–west copper lodes, together with a north–south lead course. In 1860 *Mining Journal* reported that Main Lode had been opened up by Davey's Shaft, 120yd south-east of West Bridge, and sunk vertically to 50 fathoms. Cross-cuts put out north to the lode at the 15, 28 and 40 fathom levels had all been driven a considerable distance east and west. In the 40 level, west, the lode was valued at 5 to 20 tons of ore per fathom and about 700 tons had been raised. Lead Lode, 150 fathoms east of Davey's Shaft, had at this date been seen only in a shallow adit but was shortly to be tested by another vertical shaft, named the Bedford. North Lode had similarly been opened up by a shallow adit where it was 30ft wide, with very promising indications.

The machinery on the mine comprised a 30in engine designed for pumping, crushing and drawing, with a small puffing engine on Davey's Shaft. This last had hitherto served for pumping, but on the completion of flat-rods from the 30in engine to the shaft, was to be used exclusively for hoisting.

Considering the mine had been at work for little more than two years, its progress was regarded as highly satisfactory. Moreover, as the *Mining Journal* correspondent remarked, 'What has been done has been carried out in a splendid, indeed I may say luxurious, style.'[22]

In the following year (1861) the 'richest young mine in the Tavistock district' as Crelake was then regarded, was visited by Joseph Yelloly Watson who was suitably impressed by the 'fine piles of ore, both lead and copper' to be seen on the floors and the 'remarkably fine pile of buildings on the sett – the chimney reminded me of the Nelson Monument – and the shareholders must have great confidence in the ultimate success of the mine to justify such an outlay at the commencement'.[23] Despite some degree of showmanship at surface, underground development proceeded in a miner-like way. In 1862, 270 people were employed and Davey's Shaft had been sunk to 86 fathoms, eventually reaching 116 fathoms from surface. From the 15 down to the 86 fathom cross-cut, levels were extended east–west, the longest being the 28 and 40 which were driven 300 and 225 fathoms west respectively, and extensively stoped in the backs.

Due to the discovery that Main Lode crossed the Tavy, an extension of the original lease was obtained at this time covering an area south of the river. Here Air Shaft was sunk on the underlie to 50 and another, unnamed, shaft to 28 fathoms. Meanwhile, Bedford Shaft on the Lead Lode had been deepened vertically to 70 fathoms, with levels driven north and south down to the 62. Above the 40 level, the ground was stoped away for 100 fathoms south of the shaft. No mention is made of any development on North Lode which seems to have failed in its early promise.

In 1868 the machinery consisted of a 36in pumping, crushing and jigging engine, with two steam-whims of 15 and 14in cylinder diameter. The returns showed a profit in 1867 and there was talk of negotiating a new lease. By 1870, however, the numbers employed had been reduced to 120,[24] and a few years later working ceased. Recorded outputs from 1856–74 comprised 12,000 tons of copper ore, 1,300 tons of lead ore, and 13,145oz of silver, added to which an unspecified quantity of arsenic and pyrite is known to have been raised.[25]

East of Tavistock
Two miles east of Tavistock on the Moretonhampstead road-(OS 106 NW), the discovery was made in June 1851 of a gate post showing impregnations of copper. Trifling as this incident might now appear it caused a speculative fever which resulted in a company, called Wheal Gatepost, being formed in the following month. Within weeks, costeaning by means of trenches revealed a number of lodes and cross-courses on which, however, much work had already been done by the 'ancients'. Undeterred by this, a shaft was sunk to a depth of 8 fathoms and a start made on driving an adit. In September 1851 'the veritable gatepost 6ft high, hangings and all' was brought from Tavistock to London 'where it was pronounced by all mining men worthy of a place in the Crystal Palace'.[26]

More publicity followed, blocks of ore assaying 30 per cent fine copper being forwarded to the City where they were regarded 'with intense interest as the largest specimens of copper ore of such quality ever discovered in this country at surface'. Even *Mining Journal* was rash enough to support the claim that the Devon Great Consols Main Lode ran through the sett.

About this time the name of the property was changed to Devon Burra Burra, after the celebrated South Australia mine which was then making headlines. Additional capital was raised and an order placed with Messrs Gill & Rundle of the Tavistock Iron Works for a 60in cylinder engine, the largest ever constructed by that foundry. The mine was then being developed in two parts, the original Gatepost on the east and the Brake Section to the west. In the 10 fathom level the lode was stated to be 14ft wide and composed of quartz interspersed with yellow copper ore. Middle Lode, which was expected to junction with the Brake Lode, carried a leader of ore 3in wide, while South Lode at the same level had a width of 3–4ft, similarly interspersed with yellow ore. Pending erection of the engine on Brake Shaft, two water-wheels had been installed for pumping, one of these being connected to the Gatepost section so that shaft-sinking there could proceed without hindrance. Large returns of grey and malachite ores were expected from the Gatepost Lode, whilst stones of ore assaying 50 to 75 per cent copper had already been raised from the Brake Lode at a depth only of 11 or 12 fathoms below adit.[27]

By the summer of 1853 the gloss was beginning to wear off and shareholders were becoming restive. A Birmingham correspondent complained in *Mining Journal* that whilst the adventure had been more frequently mentioned than any other mine in the United Kingdom the production forecasts had proved too optimistic and 'the piles of copper ore at grass at Gatepost Shaft appeared to have vanished'. Writing from Madrid, another shareholder expressed his belief that no mine in Great Britain had promised so much and performed so little.[28]

However, work continued in a desultory manner for some years after this. In 1855–6 a lode to the east of the great cross-course received a favourable report, and a drive was started towards it at the 40 fathom level. An accident to the 'clack' (pump-valve) involving the loss of the pit-work prevented further work here. Another lode had been found in the western ground, but this had not been investigated below the 40. Lead ore was also reported in the end of the 20 fathom level and 10 tons had recently been sold. About this time the mine reached its maximum depth of 60 fathoms at White's Shaft.

In 1861, due to the retirement of two of the principal shareholders, the machinery and materials were put up for sale. These included the 60in engine in a substantial engine-house,

(*left*) All that remains of the drowned South Tamar Consols

(*right*) the stack of Lockridge Mine with its false-window effect at the top

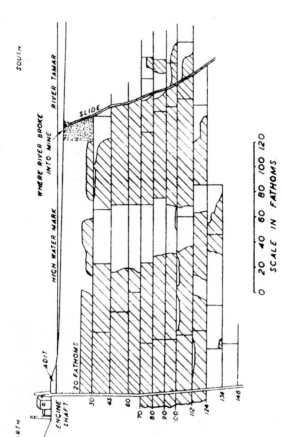

Longitudinal section of South Tamar Consols

Page 73
A group of miners in the early 1920s at Little Duke Mine in the
Tamar Valley. The site is an old stope above the twentieth level.
The 'candles' in their hats are acetylene flares

Page 74

(*above*) The mill at Tavy Consols and the suspension bridge, the cables of which are reported to have come from an old battleship being broken up at Devonport. The bridge still exists. Taken in the 1920s; (*below*) dressing-floors at Lady Bertha Mine, c1890. The bearded figure on the extreme right is Captain Skewes

150 fathoms of flat-rods and pulleys, two water-wheels (36ft by 4ft and 30ft by 3ft) with drawing and crushing machines, and twelve heads of stamps.[29] A document in the writer's possession records an output of 45 tons of low-grade copper ore in the years 1853–6. Dines quotes a figure of 190 tons in the period 1863–73. This, if true, implies a subsequent reworking, and a veritable instance of the 'triumph of hope over experience'.

On its south, Devon Burra Burra was adjoined by the sett of Wheal Surprise. Under this name, the little mine is known to have been at work in 1795 and also in 1810,[30] after which it remained in obscurity until 1851 when, due to the publicity afforded by its near neighbour, it was again taken up. The sett lay immediately west of Pennycomequick (OS 106 NW) on the south side of the stream, and was reputed to contain two copper lodes. On one of these a shaft was sunk to a 43 fathom level from surface (20 fathoms below adit) by the aid of a 30ft water-wheel erected in 1852. A few years later the mine was bankrupt but in 1856 was bought by a Mr Hill of Tavistock for £50 which, as it proved, was dear at the price. Under the new name of Whitchurch Down Consols a trifling amount of copper ore is said to have been produced, although of no marketable value. In 1859 this 'useless sett', as a contemporary critic described it, was again being offered for sale.[31] It is hard to imagine that it found a buyer.

South of Whitchurch Down lie the Sortridge Mines – Great Sortridge, Great Sortridge United, Great West Sortridge, East Sortridge, North Sortridge – which sprang up like mushrooms during the 1850s. Some of them were scarcely more than names, the companies being promoted by jobbers and merchants with little serious intention of mining. Sortridge Consols was an exception. Earlier known as West Wheal Robert, its workings lay on high ground about half a mile north of Horrabridge and nearly adjacent to Sortridge Manor (OS 106 SW). When re-opened in 1853 a rich deposit of copper ore was found only 5ft from surface, and in a matter of months £3,200 worth was sold on an outlay of £600. In 1854 the maximum depth was 30 fathoms and the lode continued as rich as ever, yielding in places 10 tons of ore per fathom. From the 20 to the 40 fathom level the course of ore returned over £50,000.[32]

At this depth the values showed a serious decline, so much so that pumping was reduced and it was actually proposed to abandon the mine. The situation was saved at the last moment by an important discovery in two of the south lodes, a fact which caused an immediate reversal of policy. In April 1855 a meeting of the shareholders authorised the installation of a new 40in engine from the Tavistock foundry of Nicholls & Williams, for the purpose of forking the old and sinking a new shaft. The existing engine, it was stated, was one of 9hp only and wholly insufficient for its task. The new engine, by contrast, was a 'noble specimen of engineering skill, combining elegance and beauty with great power'. The engine-house designed for it was similarly on the most approved principles: 'fire-proof with stairs and stair-case of iron and a flooring of slate'.

In July 1855 a colourful ceremony took place to celebrate the start of the engine's working life. At the entrance to the mine the road was crossed by a triumphal arch of evergreens, fronted by a large star formed of flowers from the four points of which floated the Union Jack and other flags. At the apex of the arch the word 'Welcome' greeted the visitors. After seeing the engine make its first stroke, the company adjourned to a dinner and settled down to listen to speeches when 'each man was supplied with his favourite beverage and a yard of clay from which quickly began to ascend clouds of smoke of the fragrant weed almost rivalling in density that issuing from the adjoining steam-engine chimney'.[33]

In the following year a sale was held of the spare materials remaining on the mine. Included in these was a curious little 11¼in high-pressure slide-valve engine of Belgian manufacture which had originally been sent to England for the Great Exhibition of 1851.[34]

After 1855 the mine continued in operation for at least another twelve years during which time the main shaft was carried down on the underlie to 152 fathoms from surface. However, little stoping or driving was done below the 62 fathom level,[35] and the mine never regained the promise of its early years. By 1866 only thirty people were employed and sales of copper ore for that year realised a mere £460. Working ceased in 1868, and a few months later the machinery comprising the 40in pumping engine, 22in winder and a 24ft water-wheel was advertised for sale.[36] Output of copper ore from 1854 to the final closure is recorded as 7,792 tons. According to Barclay and Toll, the adit (50 fathoms below surface at its deepest point) was reopened in 1883 when a quantity of low-grade tin ore was found. This continued to be worked inter-mittently and in a small way until 1902.

Great Sortridge (or Plaister Down) which was at one period included in the Sortridge Consols sett, is shown on the OS map 106 SW as a tin mine, but it produced little of that or any other mineral. By 1846 an adit had been driven 200 fathoms and was expected to cut the lode at about 12 fathoms from surface. Three shafts were later sunk, the deepest being 25 fathoms drained by a 12in engine. At that level the lode was claimed to be 8 to 14 fathoms wide and containing small quantities of tin, native copper and spots of yellow ore. It was intended that two further shafts – one on the eastern and the other on the west side of the down – be sunk with a view to taking the lode at a depth of 50 fathoms.[37] There is no evidence to suggest that this was ever carried out. The position of the mine was formerly distinguished by a tall stack which was a landmark for many miles around (Murchison, 1856). This has long since disap-peared although its base is indicated adjacent to the main shaft on the 1907 edition of the 6in map.

Immediately adjacent to Sortridge Consols on the east, but not connected underground, lay North Wheal Robert and Wheal Robert. The latter had been worked about 1825 by a local company who drove an adit 90 fathoms and sank a small shaft on one of the lodes from which 106 tons of copper ore were sold in 1825–6. Dissensions among the adventurers, coupled with the fact that the water could no longer be kept by a common hand-pump, caused the working to be abandoned.[38]

Towards the end of 1850 a London company was formed. Shortly afterwards North Wheal Robert was amalgamated with the neighbouring East Wheal Robert and the mines were subsequently operated under the general title of North Robert. Two new shafts, Murchison's and Halket's, were started at this time and orders placed for a 40ft water-wheel and 240 fathoms of flat-rods, together with the necessary pumps. Water to drive this and other wheels in the vicinity was supplied by the six-mile-long Grimstone and Sortridge leat which, as reported in *Mining Journal*, was frozen up in the severe weather of February 1853.

Although the mines produced some tin, together with small quantities of lead ore and pyrite, their output consisted mainly of copper, of which they returned 3,674 tons in the years 1853–7.[39] On the western mine, ie the original North Robert, the principal shaft was sunk on the underlie to an 80 fathom level below surface; while Murchison's Shaft on the eastern mine developed the lode vertically to 62 fathoms. By 1868 both parts of the mine had become poor, the copper shoots of the main lode having apparently been bottomed, while the tin content was too small for them to be worked solely for that mineral.[40] The materials and machinery as advertised for sale in October and December of that year comprised a 33in engine for pumping and stamping on the western mine and the 40ft wheel on the eastern mine.

The earliest reference to Willsworthy Mine, which hitherto had been unidentified, occurs in the MS of John Swete in 1797–8.

A miner (who has long been a labourer with me) informs me that between 20 and 30 years ago [say 1770] he was pursuing

78

a copper lode on an estate belonging to Mr. Tolcher of Plymouth when on a sudden by sinking his pick axe into a sort of Gossan (which was, as it were, intermixed with the lode) a body of cobalt fell and with it a quantity of water ... From this copper mine of Sampford Spiney four tons at least of cobalt was taken, of which 1,700 lbs was sent to London and sold. Like the Bohemian ore, the cobalt was impregnated with hairs and tresses of the purest silver.[41]

In 1775 Josiah Wedgwood, the potter, visited the mine on his way to Cornwall, being accompanied by Mr Tolcher then a lively, if somewhat querulous, old gentleman nearly ninety years of age. The mine was idle at this time but Wedgwood obtained from Mr Tolcher several specimens of 'what he called cobalt – but I never could bring any blue colour out of it. I have since had a whole cask of this mineral ... from Mr Gullett of Exeter, a partner in the mine, but could not find a grain of cobalt in it'.[42] Despite this, the presence of cobalt in the ore is an established fact. In an undated letter c1790, Phillip Rashleigh wrote to his fellow Cornishman and mineralogist, John Hawkins: 'When you returned by way of Tavistock, you might have gone to Hiccary Bridge [Huckworthy Bridge] and seen the Cobalt ore there frequently intermixed with small Capillary Native Silver. I have oftened wondered this mine has not been worked again, tho' the water is very powerful in it.'[43]

In fact, the mine was reopened sometime before 1814, in which year it appears for the first time under the name of Willsworthy and was advertising the sale of 'about Two Tons of Rich and Elegant Cobalt Ore which forms the purest Calx [cobalt oxide produced by reduction]. The ore will be shown on application to W. Willcox Esq of Huckworthy Bridge'.[44] (OS 106 SW).

Although the quantity was small and of no great economic importance, the occurrence of such an ore in a British mine aroused widespread interest in the scientific world of the day. Specimens were eagerly sought not merely by local mineral collectors, but also in London whither they were sent 'for the inspection of the learned in Chemistry and Mineralogy'. About this time Mr Mawe, the mineral dealer, was said to have had 200 such specimens at his shop in The Strand. One of the finest specimens in Cornwall was in the possession of Mr Arthur Penrose of Truro, assay master and agent for the Crown Copper Company. The capillary silver in this stone was described as 'springing from a fine white quartz intermixed with peach blossom arsenical cobalt'. In May 1816 the *Cornwall Gazette* announced that a stone weighing 124lb would shortly be exhibited at the British Museum. 'The Egyptian Museum in Piccadilly will also be enriched with some choice specimens ... which although hitherto unknown in this country exactly correspond with that described by Aikin as raised in the silver mines of Peru.'[45]

A description of the ore as it was seen in the lode was given by Joseph Carne, the Cornish mineralogist, in his well-known paper 'On the Discovery of Silver in the Mines of Cornwall', published in 1818:

> It occurred in Willsworthy Mine (which, indeed, may be said to be rather on the border of Devon) in 1816. The lode in which it was found was about 12in wide, bearing NNE and SSW and underlies 2½ft to the fathom, south. In the ten fathoms level, a vein of white amethystine quartz divided the lode: between this vein of quartz ... and the north wall of the lode was found a vein of rich arsenical cobalt ore, combined with native capillary silver in a ferruginous matrix from three to six inches wide. The space between the vein of quartz ... and the southern wall of the lode was occupied by a vein of rich yellow copper ore, from six to nine inches wide. The silver continued about six fathoms in length and was not seen deeper. The copper was not so soon exhausted. The specimens of native silver from this mine have eclipsed all that have ever before been found in Cornwall, both in size and beauty.[46]

It is evident from the above that Carne himself was not personally acquainted with the mine and was uncertain as to its site. This is surprising in view of the explicit statement in the contemporary Cornish press that it lay at Huckworthy Bridge in the parishes of Sampford Spiney and Walkhampton[47] – a statement which in fact has passed unnoticed to the present day. As a consequence Dines (along with others) has assumed that the mine was probably situated on a farm named Willsworthy some $2\frac{1}{2}$ miles north-east of Mary Tavy although, as he admits, no trace of mining has been seen there.[48] The Willsworthy Mine ceased working in 1817, consequent on a number of the shareholders failing to meet their calls. The materials as advertised for sale included a 35ft diameter water-wheel, 20 fathoms of pumps and a horse-whim.[49]

Under the name of Huckworthy Bridge, some further activity took place in the 1840s and again in 1860–1, an output of 23 tons of copper ore being recorded in the latter period. The mine was then 40 fathoms deep from surface and had a 40ft diameter wheel driving pumps and a crusher. Operations were abandoned in December 1862 when the plant was offered for sale in *Mining Journal*.

In the immediate vicinity of Huckworthy Bridge, prospecting trials were carried out on a number of other lodes. Among these was Wheal Collier where, in 1846, a deep cross-cut adit was being driven north from the Walkham River to intersect the lodes of the Huckworthy Bridge Mine. Another adit was also driven on a copper lode further to the north. 'Our contiguity to the old Huckworthy Mine which returned some of the richest copper ever produced in the county and also cobalt of very good quality', was claimed to give added value to the Wheal Collier sett. Little more is heard of the latter mine which had earlier been worked by the Plymouth and Dartmoor Mining Company.[50]

A short distance downstream from Huckworthy Bridge, East Wheal George (OS 112 NW) was started in 1849 when a lode carrying a rich vein of copper was discovered at only 10ft from surface. On this a shaft was started on the southern margin of the river and was eventually sunk to a depth of 60 fathoms. In 1850–2 the mine returned 660 tons of ore, averaging nearly 14 per cent copper.[51] Most of the stoping was done between surface and the 22 fathom level, below this the values declined and the levels became successively shorter. Two dumps of considerable size were still standing near this shaft in 1959. On the further bank of the river, North Lode was opened up by a shaft sunk to 20 fathoms. The mine was drained by a 40ft water-wheel and, according to local tradition, was eventually flooded by being stoped too close beneath the river bed. Working ceased in 1858 when the output of East Wheal George amounted to 783 tons of ore which sold for £6,480 (figures compiled by Justin Brooke).

The principal copper mine of this district was Wheal Franco whose workings lay a short distance west of Horrabridge (OS 112 NW). The sett was a large one, extending along the south bank of the River Walkham, with an older portion on the western side of the Plymouth to Tavistock road. In this latter area, known as Old Wheal Franco, work had started by 1823 and in the course of the next twenty years the mine was developed to a depth of 160 fathoms. In 1838, 1,461 tons of ore were returned to the value of £5,078, 133 people were employed and there were six water-wheels varying in size from 14 to 32ft diameter.[52]

By 1843, when it had produced some £60,000 worth of ore, this part of the sett was thought to be exhausted and a new shaft was started on a rich course of ore to the east of the road, which henceforth became the active centre of the mine. In 1846, 140 tons of ore were being raised monthly and in the following years Engine Shaft was carried down vertically to 110 fathoms from surface, while six other shafts had been sunk on the property. With varying degrees of fortune, operations continued until 1862, by which date 10,333 tons of ore had been sold for £51,500.[53]

In 1870 Wheal Franco Consols was formed to acquire the

properties formerly worked as Old and New Franco. Between these lay a piece of virgin ground containing three lodes of black and grey copper ore which had beeen intersected in a cutting of the Plymouth and Tavistock railway. To develop this ground, Sutton's Shaft was being sunk in May 1870, while an adit, already driven 70 fathoms south from the Walkham River, was then within 22 fathoms of the shaft which it would drain to a depth of 23 fathoms. South of the shaft, the adit was expected to cut four other lodes and to give backs of over 64 fathoms. In the spring of 1871, 70 tons of ore were sold for £102, but soon after this transaction was effected the mine was abandoned.[54]

About half a mile south of Horrabridge, Furzehill Mine in Furzehill Wood (OS 112 NW) was reopened in 1860 on the strength of its erstwhile reputation for tin. Known to have been worked extensively in the eighteenth century and possibly far earlier, it had two adits; one 6 fathoms and the other 11 fathoms deep – the latter driven 500 fathoms across the strike of the lodes. A correspondent in *Mining Journal* stated that these had not been worked to any extent:

since the time of 'Bal Hatchett', the noted miner of bygone times but it seems to have been one of his favourites of several wrought at that period. The antiquated mode of working then adopted – round shafts, shafts shammelled from the surface in steps to save tackles and ropes, immense open cuttings, and the many concave-sided stones for pulverising the tin – as also the trees now overgrowing the whole workings – are all indicative of a remote age. It appears to have been the practice to under-let numerous small takings of ground to pares of men for a certain length on the lodes, to be worked from the surface as now in the Australian gold fields. By this great division of labour, coupled with the assistance of a cross-cut adit driven more than half a mile in length, they coped with the water and drew the tin-stuff through some 30 shafts to surface and thereby sold at least £30,000 worth of tin despite the then low price of the metal and the three-fold cost of working in comparison with more modern methods[55].

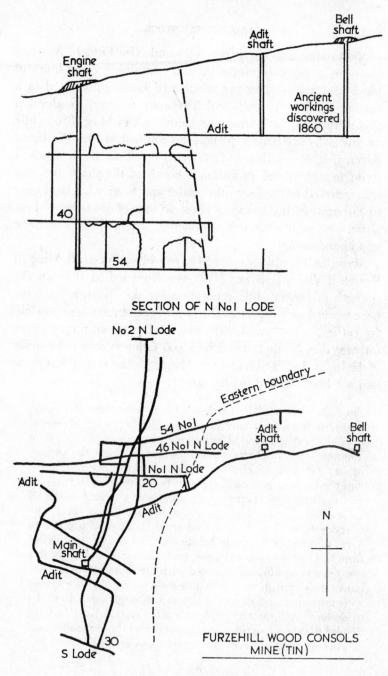

SECTION OF N No1 LODE

Plan of Furzehill Mine, Horrabridge

Soon after its inception, the new company set about sinking an engine-shaft. At a shallow depth this passed through a lode estimated to be worth £25 per fathom, whilst four other lodes were expected to be reached by means of short cross-cuts. By 1867 the shaft had been sunk to 54 fathoms giving access to old men's levels in which the supporting pillars (arches) were valued at 44lb of black tin to the ton. From these, 21 tons of concentrate were sold for £1,053 in 1866.[56]

In a maze of irregular workings, exploratory work of this nature was not without danger, and in the following year seven men and a boy were drowned when the 40 fathom level unexpectedly holed into an old flooded gunnis. Due to the low price of tin, operations were suspended in 1868 when the machinery consisting of a 30ft water-wheel and a 24in rotary steam engine for pumping, winding and stamping was offered for sale.

Working was resumed at Furzehill Tin Mine in 1870 and the company was still on the active list in 1879 (although latterly it would seem to small advantage). But recorded output from 1862–77 amounted only to 196 tons of black tin and 2 tons of arsenic (Dines p 700).

Today, the old 'coffan' or open-cast workings, with the numerous unfenced shafts of both latter days and more recent times appear but little changed – although more treacherously disguised than formerly by the dense bracken which has invaded the woodland.

CENTRAL DARTMOOR

On Yennadon Down, 1½ miles east-north-east of Yelverton, a lode has been worked for iron ore in the Yennadon Mine (OS 112 NW). Advertised for sale in 1838, it was stated that the Plymouth and Dartmoor Tramway passed through the sett at two different levels and that in addition to iron-stone, manganese had been discovered, as had several copper and tin lodes which could be worked at a small outlay. By 1847 an adit had been driven upwards of 60 fathoms and was then approaching one of the lodes which it was expected to cut at 11 fathoms deep. The lode at surface was about 12ft wide and appeared to have been worked by the old men to a depth of 12ft where rocks of tin stuff had been found. Recent blasting of the ore body showed good leaders or branches of cassiterite running through it.[57]

To the east, tin has been worked in numerous small lodes traversing the high moorland area. The deposits, being situated in the heart of the granite country, constitute the bottom part of the tin-bearing zone – the 'roots' of lodes which had once extended upwards into the overlying killas before being swept away in the long process of denudation of the latter following post-Carboniferous times. Their outcrops, where exposed in the existing land surface, would have been clearly recognisable to the alluvial tinners as they roamed the moors, but the mines in which they were subsequently developed have necessarily proved to be as limited in depth as in productiveness.

In 1823 the lease was advertised of some 400 acres of land in the moorland parish of Sheepstor, together with underlying minerals consisting of tin, copper, manganese, cobalt, silver, lead and china clay.[58] To this list, gold might well have been added since it is recorded about this time that a miner called Wellington obtained £40 worth of the precious metal from an unspecified site in Sheepstor. This he sold to a Plymouth silversmith named Pearce – the discovery being claimed as the largest deposit of gold ever found on Dartmoor.[59]

Characteristic of other small lode workings of this area was the Kit Tin Mine which lay a few hundred yards south-east of Sheepstor church (OS 112 NE). No records have been found of the early history of the mine which was last tried in 1915 when the adit was reopened and a shaft sunk to 60ft. According to the Barclay MS the cassiterite occurred in quartz strings, in a country rock consisting of killas overlying the granite. The ore was treated by six heads of stamps which were still in existence (and photographed) in 1928. Only the wheel-pit now remains, together with two buddles and the former blacksmith's shop, these being situated near the Sheepstor Brook, a little to the west of Collyton.[60]

Half a mile east of the Rain Gauge shown on Yellowmead Down and immediately south of Outholme Wood the site of an old shaft is marked on the OS map 112 NE. An adit communicates with this shaft, with traces of a tram road extending from its mouth. The adit is said to have been driven about 1870 in search of china clay,[61] but probably served an earlier purpose as a tin trial, alluvial stream workings being visible throughout the length of the Narrator Brook which flows hardby.

By comparison with these small trials, Eyelesborough or Eylesbarrow (pronounced Ailsboro), some two miles north-east of Sheepstor, was a tin mine of some importance, but records of its output are lacking and there are no known plans of the underground workings. The mine was at work in 1823 when, along with Vitifer and Whiteworks, it ranked among the few mines then active on Dartmoor. It had the further distinction of owning a smelting house where 100 blocks of tin metal were coined in the Michaelmas quarter of 1824.[62] Under the name of Dartmoor Consolidated, exploratory work was in progress from 1838 until 1844 when due to the low price of black tin (£40 per ton) and the difficulty of renewing the lease, operations were suspended after returns of over £30,000 had been made.

Work was resumed in 1847 consequent on a favourable report by Captain John Spargo of Stoke Climsland who recommended the deepening of Pryce Deacon's Shaft by 20 fathoms into more settled country. He also noted that small fibres of wolfram (known by the miners as cockle) were dropping towards the lode which, owing to water and the softness of the ground, had hitherto been scarcely worked below the adit level. About £3,000 was needed to reopen the mine on which there was a large 'mansion house', a dwelling for the captain, a smelting house, smith's shop and other buildings. In May 1847, Two Brothers' Adit was being cleared and the manager reported that the deep adit driven by the old adventurers had been cleared to Pryce Deacon's Shaft, which came down on the adit-end 600 fathoms from its mouth. Other shafts mentioned at this time included, from west to east, Whim, New Engine, Old Engine and Henry's, the whole of the workings being drained by a 50ft overshot wheel.[63] In 1848 it was decided to abandon the mine, which was largely controlled by shareholders living in Great Coggeshall, Essex, the expenses by this time having greatly exceeded the original estimate.

In 1849 working was renewed as Aylesborough. During that year it was reported that Henry's Shaft was down to 20 fathoms below adit, which was 10 fathoms deeper than any of the previous workings. In the last 10 fathoms of sinking, the shaft was producing 'good work for tin' and the men were then starting to drive on the lode. In the 10 fathom level, east, the lode was also producing good ore and appeared to be getting under the run of tin ground seen in the bottom of the ancient workings. The main bunch, however, from which the earlier company had made their returns, was still about 10 fathoms further east. In driving west, the lode was disordered by a slide, producing a little tin but not rich.[64] The mine at this date had six heads of stamp.

In April 1851 the company was refloated as Wheal Ruth Tin Mine. The prospectus tallied in nearly all respects with that of Eyelesborough, repeating earlier statements that thousands of pounds had been spent in sinking shafts, driving cross-cuts and bringing up adits, and that 600 fathoms had been driven on the course of the lodes which lay in decomposed granite. The ore was claimed to be superior in quality to any other in Devon, consisting of grain tin which had a market value of £15 per ton in excess of common tin. A report issued by Jehu Hitchins at this time states that principal operations had hitherto been confined to: (*a*) Michaelmas Shaft Lode, otherwise South Lode; (*b*) Aylesborough North Lode, and (*c*) Middle Lode, 'near to Wheal Kate'.

A new Engine Shaft, then sinking on the north of the property, had reached a depth of 13 fathoms under adit and in June 1851 the lode in the 12 fathom level, east, was 2½ft wide and worth £17 per fathom. Six months later the shaft was down to 24 fathoms below the 30 fathom deep adit. By the following May, however, operations had ceased and the sale was advertised of the whole of the machinery and materials consisting of the 50ft by 3ft water-wheel, 30 fathoms of whim-ropes, a 17ft wheel with six heads of stamps, and 70 fathoms of ladders.[65] No mention is made of the smelting house which may have continued in operation for some time after this, purchasing tin concentrates from other mines such as Vitifer and Bottle Hill.

The surface features of Eylesbarrow today consist of some fairly extensive open-cast workings on adjacent high ground and the ruins of an erstwhile farmhouse – no doubt the 'mansion' referred to in the 1847 report. From here, the dressing-floors of the mine can be traced down the eastern slope of Drizzlecombe, along with the sites of stamping mills, settling pools and the dry courses of the leats serving them. On the north side of the track approaching the mine from the west, may be seen a double row of short granite posts with grooves chiselled in their tops. The purpose of this alignment has sometimes been questioned but there is little doubt that it supported a series of rollers which eased the oscillatory movement of the rods, the grooves serving as bearings for the axles of the rollers. Traces of solidified animal grease, used as a lubricant, can still be seen on some of the granite posts.

The smelting works lay on the western side of the Drizzlecombe stream where it is marked on the OS map 112 NE as a blowing-house. Careful examination of the ruins by Hansford Worth showed that the internal dimensions of the building measured 60ft by 20ft, with a flue of over 70ft in length extending from the north wall. This layout differed materially from any of the forty known open-hearth blowing-houses situated elsewhere on the moor, whilst the Eylesbarrow slag was also of a different character due to lime having been used as a flux.[66] From existing evidence it thus seems clear that the smelting was carried out here in a reverberatory-type furnace which despite its introduction to Cornwall early in the 1700s was apparently unknown in Devon before the last century.

Approximately one mile north-east of Eylesbarrow lies the Nun's Cross Mine (OS 113 NW). A tin work adjacent to the 'cross of St Siward' (Nun's Cross) is referred to in a document of 1343,[67] but it is now impossible to say whether this related to an alluvial stream or an open-cast lode working. The mining sett granted during the last century was stated to contain three east-west tin lodes and two caunter lodes, all of which showed signs of having been extensively developed on the backs by the old men.

In 1862–4 exploratory work was carried out on these by a small cost-book company. Investigations revealed two long cross-cut adits driven at shallow depths, whilst on one of the caunter lodes a third adit, some 10 fathoms deeper, was found to carry fair values for tin. It was estimated that £500 would be needed to clear this adit and sink ventilation shafts. In June 1863 it was reported that a shaft then sinking from surface would shortly reach the adit level when driving would be resumed. A sum of £10 was also voted for exploring other lodes which it might seem advisable to work, more especially since a rich branch had recently been laid open in the Devonport leat tunnel which passed through the sett. About 30 fathoms remained to drive in the adit before reaching the Nun's or Main Lode where hopes were entertained of finding good values when it was intersected below the old bottoms.[68] Operations, however, appear to have ceased before the end of 1864 without recorded production.

Page 91
(*above*) Water-wheel and Cornish stamps at Golden Dagger Mine,
1937; (*below*) traces of a disturbed copper lode appear in the roof of
the Tavistock Canal at this point – a few yards in from the northern
entrance at Crebor

(*above*) Engine-house and stack of West Wheal Crebor near Gulworthy. The engine-house was demolished a few years ago and the stack was destroyed earlier; (*below*) this photograph, taken about 1870, shows what are believed to be piles of ore from Crelake Mine at the GWR Tavistock South station. The mine had an arrangement with the old South Devon Railway to transport its ores cheaply

Some two miles south-east of Princetown, the high moorland tract of Foxtor Mires comprises the source of the River Swincombe. Throughout the centuries the area had been worked for alluvial tin, in the course of which numerous small lodes were laid bare in the decomposed granite forming the bed-rock. By the late eighteenth century, if not earlier, underground development of these lodes had been started in the White Works Mine (OS 107 SW). Due to the topography of the area, the adits by which it was mainly exploited were rarely more than a few fathoms below surface, while the swampy nature of the ground, combined with the primitive pumping facilities of that time, prevented shaft-sinking to any significant depth. In 1808, the mine with its several 'workmen's cottages, capital water-engine, pumps, rods, and stamping mills' was advertised for sale,[69] having produced considerable, though unspecified, quantities of tin in its late working.

The mine is known to have been active again in 1820–6, and subsequently in 1848 when it operated for some years under the name of Wheal Industry. During this period, adits were further extended on several of the lodes and at least one new shaft was sunk. In February 1852 two-thirds of the mine was offered for sale by H. Bickford of Princetown, a principal partner in the concern. The sett at this time was stated to contain twenty-four lodes, from which the existing proprietors had divided over £500 worth of tin, and a prospective purchaser might expect to receive an income of £25 per cent per annum on his outlay.[70] It is not known whether the sale took place, but the mine itself continued in operation until 1863.

In 1868 the property reverted to its original name of White Works when a new company was formed and registered at Truro. Under the pursership of Moses Bawden of Tavistock, work started in April of the following year when preparations were being made for sinking and opening up the sett on a large scale. Two parcels of excellent-quality black tin were sold in January 1870, and by December 1871 over 29 tons had been returned for £2,234. In the early part of 1872 the mine was taken over by another company of similar name and in 1876 96 tons of concentrate was said to have been sold. Although the plan of the workings as described by Dines shows no developments below adit, it was announced in 1877 that the mine had been sunk to 30 fathoms.[71] This was obviously deeper than all the known adits and probably represents the greatest depth attained by any of the fifteen or more shafts shown on the 1883–4 edition of the 6in map.

Bachelor's Hall Mine (OS 107 SW, NW), three-quarters of a mile east of Princetown, was started early in the 1790s following the discovery of a tin lode when cutting the Dock (ie Devonport) Leat. On this a shaft was sunk by Mr Gray, the owner of the estate, who subsequently erected a stamping mill and a smelting house on the banks of a small stream which empties into the Blackabrook. John Swete, who visited the mine shortly before 1797, states that it was then employing sixteen men 'two of whom worked the windlass over the shaft'.[72] Soon after this, misunderstandings arose with Sir Thomas Tyrwhitt of Tor Royal, in consequence of which operations were abandoned.

On the expiry of the original lease, Sir Thomas proposed to work the mine himself, but found difficulty in forking the water, 'the main rod of the engine was cut off just below the bob plat, leaving the pumps and pit-work standing in the shaft'. This small concern possessed a beam pumping engine, and this can only be explained by its altitude which rendered it impossible to obtain the water-power that was normally used in preference to steam in all save the largest mines of Devon.

For some time after the sett remained idle, but in 1845 a new company was formed with a twenty-one year lease from the Duchy. Its first task was to clear a deep adit which had earlier been started from the Blackabrook with the object of developing the mine 12 fathoms below the bottom of the Engine Shaft (33 fathoms from surface) where a large extent of tin ground was believed to be standing. The adit was 7ft high and

3ft wide, and by 1846 had been cleared for a length of 60 fathoms. At this point lack of funds, combined with 'disgraceful and almost unheard of mismanagement', brought the project to a close.

Two further attempts were subsequently made to reopen the property where the tin had the reputation of fetching a higher price than any other mine on the moor. In 1853 a report by J. Sims, of the Slimeford Office, Calstock, claimed with some exaggeration that Engine Shaft was then down to 50 fathoms and that the deep adit on completion would unwater the mine 30 fathoms below the existing bottom. There was also a second shaft on the property named Ann's, which had been sunk to the level of the shallow adit. In 1862 it was announced that only 120 fathoms remained to drive in the Deep Adit in order to bring it under the old workings. This could be achieved for a relatively small sum as the lode in the adit end was 2½ft wide and producing good tin stuff. The shallow adit had been driven on a parallel lode close alongside and this could be developed by short cross-cuts from the deep adit.[73] There is nothing to suggest that any of these proposals bore fruit and the plan of the mine, as described by Dines, shows Deep Adit as being stopped 200 fathoms short of its intended objective.

In 1797 it was noted by John Swete that tin ore had recently been found on the tenement of Brimpts adjoining the west bank of the East Dart River, about half a mile north of Dartmeet (OS 107 NE). Work started soon afterwards as evidenced in the following manifesto published in *Mining Journal*, 8 September 1849:

I, Richard Tuckett of Dunnabridge, in the parish of Lydford do solemnly declare that I am now 79 years of age and that about 50 years since I was in the service of Mr Joseph Sanders of Brimpts and that whilst in his employ I was in the habit of drawing with a slide-but tin stuff from the shaft near to the stable, and also from a level in a field called the Potatoe Field, part of Brimpts estate, down to the stamps, and I continued

drawing tin stuff from these places for two or three years. And
I further declare that I remember the mine at Brimpts being
worked by Joseph Sanders alone for 7 or 8 years and that the
tin stuff when made marketable was taken to Tavistock, and
I further declare that Joseph Sanders discontinued working the
mine because he considered that the miners were imposing on
him, and I recollect that the miners offered to work the mine at
a low tribute but that Joseph Sanders refused their application.

A report by Jehu Hitchins in July 1849 states that rich stones
of ore were then to be found in the ancient open-workings,
below which the old men had excavated the lode to a depth of
10 fathoms under the adit. He advised the immediate erection
of a water-wheel and that the adit should be cleared and extended. Work started in September of that year, and by March
1850 the adit had been secured for 45 fathoms and was then
within 3 fathoms of the Engine Shaft. Sales of tin nearly
covered costs, as reported in August and November 1850, but
this statement was subsequently denied at a stormy meeting
of the adventurers.

In common with others on the moor, the Brimpts sett
was extensive – two and three quarter miles on the course of
the lodes and bounded on the south and east by the West and
East Dart Rivers, and on the west by the Cherry Brook. Not
content with this, the adventurers obtained additional ground
in September 1851, extending north to Bellever Tor. At the
same time a call was made to provide a new water-wheel with
an additional twelve heads of stamps. The company was now in
financial difficulties, and in May 1852 the materials including
two water-wheels of 28 and 25ft diameter, 270 fathoms of
flat-rods, two lifts of pumps, six heads of stamps and a horse-
whim were offered for sale.

The sett and materials were acquired by a new company,
the Duke of Cornwall Consolidated Tin Mines, which resumed
operations in the same year. The property at this time consisted of two parts, known as the North and the South Mine.

The former lay on the summit of the hill where a lode underlying steeply south was developed by a vertical shaft 15 fathoms deep. This was drained by a 24ft wheel connected to the pumps by nearly 200 fathoms of flat-rods. South Mine on the side of the hill comprised three east-west lodes which had been intersected by a shallow cross-cut adit. The more important of these was South Lode on which a shaft was sunk to an eventual depth of 45 fathoms, the water being drawn by a 28ft diameter wheel operating 75 fathoms of flat-rods. Some 32 fathoms below the shallow adit, a deep adit had been started from the river but it appears that the latter was never driven far enough to connect with the South Lode workings.[74]

Owing to many of the shareholders failing to meet their calls, the Duke of Cornwall Mine survived for only one year, and in 1853 the sett was taken over by a company named Devon Tin Mines. Two hundred sacks of tin stuff were raised from a 5 fathom level during June of that year, and work was also proceeding in the 15 fathom level on North Mine. In November it was agreed to lease an area of ground from the Duchy on which to erect a residence for the manager and houses for the miners.

By January 1855, Engine Shaft on North Mine had been deepened to 26 fathoms, the last 15 fathoms being in good tin ground. Six heads of stamps were at work, and some 23cwt of black tin had been sold at the rate of £42 10s per ton. At a meeting held in July 1855 it was resolved to wind up the company. Justin Brooke has suggested that this decision was possibly due to the failure of its bankers, Strahan Paul & Co.[75] Collins records sales to the value of £1,363 during the final year of working, part of which may have come from the Arundell or Druid Mine near Ashburton which was under the same management.

About half a mile west of Hexworthy village (OS 107 SE) tin has been worked for centuries in the valley of the Swincombe River. Here, as elsewhere, development followed the usual pattern. The original streaming era is represented at Gobbett by a well-preserved blowing-house complete with a crazing-mill, moulds for casting the smelted ingots and a leat from the river to drive the wheel operating the bellows. Extending along the south side of the road from the village, an excavation 15 to 20yd wide and 15ft deep illustrates the next stage when a lode was worked open-cast, possibly with the addition of small shafts. Finally, the lodes were exploited solely by underground mining in Wheal Gobbett, Deby Hole and Wheal Compton (or Cumpston).

In the years 1836–40, when operating under the name of Dartmoor United Tin Mines, a shaft was sunk in the Gobbett section to a depth of 40 fathoms. From this levels extended on the course of the lodes yielded black tin to the value of £1,000. The machinery consisted of two 24ft diameter water-wheels, one being used for pumping and the other for driving stamps. Further development of the mines being hindered by disagreement among the adventurers, the property was offered for sale in 1840 and resumed work shortly afterwards as Dartmoor Consols. In the course of the next two years an adit was driven 150 fathoms on a lode which is said to have produced some 20 tons of concentrate.[76]

In the late 1860s, the sett was once more taken up when it was known for a time as Swincombe Vale. By 1874 the Engine Shaft had been cleared to a depth of 12 fathoms below adit (7 fathoms) and levels were being driven east and west with a view to finding new ore ground. The old water-wheel still standing on the mine was then in a 'feeble state' and a new wheel was about to be erected. Apart from this there was sufficient machinery on the sett to raise and dress 20 tons of ore a day. A grade of 1 per cent would render this viable, although considerably higher values were anticipated. The ore was said to be free from sulphides and $1\frac{1}{2}$ tons of concentrate were then ready for sale. It was intended in due course to sink the shaft to 10 or 12 fathoms below the existing bottoms.[77] Despite this favourable report it would appear that little more was done and no record of production has been found for this latest working.

The site of the Gobbett Mine is shown on the 6in map, but the whereabouts of Deby Hole and Wheal Compton are no longer identifiable, although the latter is thought to have been in the neighbourhood of Huccaby.

Hens Roost Mine as it is marked on the OS map 107 SE, is now more generally known as Hexworthy, a rather misleading title since it lies fully a mile south-east of that village on the borders of Holne Moor. The mine originated as a group of old men's outcrop workings, comprising Hens Roost on the north and Hooten Wheals to the south.

In 1854 it was reported that the lode in the former had been worked for 40 to 50 fathoms in length and to 30 fathoms in depth, partly as an open-cutting, and below this by back-stoping from an adit driven beneath. On the southern lodes the workings extended for three-quarters of a mile and were excavated in a similar fashion by the ancient miners to a depth of 20 fathoms. During 1852–5 exploratory work was carried out in the sett by a company which expended £4,000 in clearing adits and sinking a new shaft on which a 42in steam engine was erected. In one of the adits a small lode or branch was found, 5 to 6in wide, from which about 8cwt of black tin was sold in August 1854. The surface works included the construction of dressing-floors, erecting a 30ft wheel with eight heads of stamps and laying a tramway from the shaft to the floors. In July 1855, as a consequence of dissension among the shareholders, the mine and materials were advertised for sale, although it was considered 'by competent judges, that with a few months' spirited working they would pay costs and shortly after make profits'.[78]

A fresh start was made in 1891 when John Taylor & Sons, the well-known firm of mining engineers, were appointed to lay out the property. A report issued by the company towards the end of that year stresses the exceptional difficulties encountered in reopening the mine where due to its situation 'in a bleak and desolate region in the heart of Dartmoor', roads had to be cut for the transport of machinery and houses erected for the accommodation of the men.

Despite this, much had been accomplished. Taylor's Shaft had been sunk to 24 fathoms and an adit driven 170 fathoms. A 12 head battery of stamps was then at work, and two wheels of 21 and 30ft diameter had been erected for pumping and stamping – water for these being obtained from the O Brook which passed through the sett. No steam power had yet been required, but an engine had been placed near the stamps for use as an auxiliary in case of need. Production of black tin in 1891 amounted to 18 tons 7cwt, which sold at the rate of £60 per ton against an average price for that year of £50 15s.[79] Working continued until 1896 when tin (metal) reached an all-time low of £63 per ton. Output to this date had amounted to 135 tons of black tin which realised £7,525.

With the recovery in price to £143 per ton, operations were renewed in 1905 and from December 1907 to June 1909 1,717 tons of ore were crushed and 54 tons of concentrate sold for £3,716 at a working cost of approximately £2,500. Owing to the coarse nature of the cassiterite, the treatment was very simple. The pulp from the stamps was passed through classifiers to Wilfley tables and the slimes to round frames and thence to buddles; final dressing was carried out by tossing and packing in kieves. During this period Californian stamps were employed and the mine was electrified, power being generated by a Pelton Wheel near Saddle Bridge, a mile downstream from the mill and a short distance from the confluence of the O Brook with the West Dart River.

Due to lack of capital and hand-to-mouth methods, the plant only worked for eight hours daily and in 1912 a Mr E. S. King, then consulting engineer to a number of mines in Cornwall, was called in to suggest improvements. He reported that there were three lodes in the mine. The most important of these was Low's Lode which was being worked at adit and in the 12 and 24 fathom levels. In the latter, the lode averaged 19½in wide over a length of 1,400ft, with a mean value of 37lb of black tin to the ton. In the following year, on Mr King's recommendation, the shaft was sunk a further 120ft, where the lode showed improvement both in size and value. The work was completed at the outbreak of World War I when further progress was prevented by the call-up of men for the services. The mine was then placed under care and maintenance and the last recorded production was 13¼ tons of black tin in 1915–16.

During the winter of 1920, a rainstorm of exceptional violence destroyed the flume carrying water to the pumping wheel, and the mine became flooded. In 1925 proposals were made for a reopening, with the addition of a further ten heads of stamps in order to double output.[80] It would appear that nothing came of this suggestion, and the use of the site for combat practice by American forces during World War II destroyed most of the buildings which were left.

Birch Tor and Vitifer

Near the fourteenth milestone from Tavistock, on the Moreton-hampstead road, an area comprising some two square miles formerly constituted the largest tin-producing region of Dartmoor. Here can be seen the great gullies or open-cast workings excavated over the centuries by alluvial streamers; whilst all around stand traces of adits, shafts, leats and wheel-pits, together with ruined buildings formerly housing the stamps and treatment plant of a later period of mining. In contrast to its former activity, the area now lies silent and deserted amid the solitude of the moor, with heather and bracken regaining their old ascendancy over the work of man.

Chief among the mines of this locality were Birch Tor and Vitifer, the latter first described by Charles Hatchett, the eighteenth-century geologist and mineralogist, who visited the mine in 1796. He observed that the lode ran east to west, and had already been developed for over a quarter of a mile in length, as seen in the 'antient channels' cut down upon it in former times by streaming. The country rock consisted of pale-red decomposed granite or growan, in which the lode varied in width from one to twenty or more inches. The tin occurred in a matrix of quartz, often accompanied by black schorl, also with peach or chlorite of different tints of green. The cassiterite consisted of small prisms of pale-brown colour 'frequently coated with a brown earthy tin somewhat resembling Wood Tin'. Alongside the walls of the lode there generally ran a thin vein of Eisenglimmer (specular haematite). This iron ore was also found in larger quantities within the body of the lode, and was sold separately to a Mr Kingdon, the lessee of the sett, who had evidently found a market for the product. The tin concentrates were sent to Tavistock where there was a small smelting works owned by a Mr Lane. The mine at this time was employing forty men and had thirteen shafts. Engine Shaft was 21 fathoms deep with an over-shot wheel for pumping, whilst Western Shaft was in course of sinking to a 40 fathom level.[81]

In 1808, the Vitifer Mine was advertised for sale and during the 1820s was being worked in conjunction with Birch Tor by the Davey brothers of Redruth. With tin (metal) standing at little more than £70 per ton, the times were not propitious for mining. 'I never knew things so bad here,' wrote Stephen Davey to the manager in 1826. 'Gettings among the miners are very small, I should think under 50s per month, for which they are obliged to work *very hard* [Davey's emphasis]. Now seems to be the time to work Birch Tor to advantage and I think the reduced rate of labour will more than compensate the fall in the price of tin. I don't know the quality of the tin you have been sending to Ailsboro Smelting House.'[82]

Shortly after this time the Daveys appear to have taken into their partnership a distant relative named 'Quaker' John Palk.

The latter had long been working part of Birch Tor on his own account, and was consequently better acquainted with the character of its lodes than the Daveys could have been. Having gradually worked his way into the position of manager, he continued to make call after call for money to carry on the mine and at length the patience of the Daveys became exhausted. Believing the property to be almost worthless, they offered it to Palk for a small sum. The latter equivocated. 'Friend,' he said, 'I am a poor man and cannot raise so much but by the blessing of the Lord I would like to try to earn a bit of bread from it to put into my mouth. Will thee not 'bate the price to the level of my means?' Eventually he became sole owner of the property as had been his aim all along. Although knowing full well where the best values lay, he had hitherto studiously avoided working anything but the poorest ore. Once the mine became his own its complexion showed a radical change, and he is reputed to have made an ultimate profit of £60,000 by his shrewd if unscrupulous deal.[83]

In 1838 Birch Tor was said to be the only mine of any magnitude then working on Dartmoor. Operated entirely by water-power, it had two 40ft wheels and one of 32ft and was employing 117 people, thirty of whom were women and children. The mine being situated at an altitude of 1,100 to 1,400ft above sea level, the leats supplying water for the wheels were commonly frozen up for several weeks at a time in winter. The miners consisted largely of men who had absconded from other districts on account of petty offences, and so scanty was the accommodation in the few and wretched hovels near the mine that the beds were always occupied – as one occupant left for work, he was succeeded by another returning from the mine.[84] Added to the ill effects of overcrowding, much hardship resulted from the nature of the work. This applied not only to those exposed to the weather on surface, but equally to those underground where due to the porous nature of the granite, the miners frequently laboured beneath streams of ice-cold water, a condition far more deleterious to health than the heat experienced in the close-grained rock of deeper mines.

Apparently the hardy native moormen withstood the conditions better. In 1864 it was recorded that a certain Joe Hamlyn had worked at Birch Tor for seventy-five years, and that another miner, Jacob German, had been there for sixty years. Men such as these usually had homes in one or other of the neighbouring moorland villages to which they periodically returned, bringing back food for the ensuing week and sleeping in sheds fitted with bunks provided by the mine. At the old Warren House Inn, where it is said that the peat fire never went out for 100 years, uproarious scenes were witnessed on pay days when those who could afford the dubious luxury of getting drunk indulged in countless brawls and horseplay.

In 1845 it was stated that the Vitifer Mine had been worked intermittently over a period of 150 years, and had been developed by the old men in open-cast excavations 100 to 200ft wide. A new company was formed at this time to amalgamate Vitifer and Birch Tor in a combined sett of over a mile in length. In 1846 Engine Shaft on the Birch Tor Lode was 84 fathoms deep from surface and some time later Hambly's Shaft reached a depth of 60 fathoms. During this period the mines were drained by two 45ft water-wheels, and Brunton frames were introduced for re-treating the halvans (discarded leavings). These were said to have proved effective in separating the iron ore from the tin. Generally speaking, however, the lodes were less rich than the company had been led to expect, more particularly in the deepest level (74 fathoms) where the drives extending east and west entered very poor ground.

Notwithstanding this, a fresh company was formed in 1859 entitled New Birch Tor and Vitifer Consols. In 1866 95½ tons of black tin was sold for £4,739, 120 people were employed, and the mine was stated to be profitable and likely to continue so. The two water-wheels were then pumping from a depth of 70 fathoms from surface,[85] work being concentrated on three lodes: North, Graham's and Great South Lode. For some years the output enabled dividends to be paid, but by the 1870s the best tin ground was becoming exhausted. After 1880 no shaft sinking or driving was carried out, and in 1886 the sett was abandoned.

In 1923 a new lease was obtained from the Duchy and a considerable sum was expended on erecting machinery and improved dressing plant. A few shallow levels were reopened, but little tin was raised. Further trials carried out in 1938-9 were chiefly confined to the treatment of dumps and tailings. The outbreak of war caused this last working to be abandoned, and since that time the sett has remained idle.[86]

East Birch Tor Mine, as its name implies, lay east of Birch Tor and Vitifer Consols. The workings were situated in the valley between Headland Warren and Challacombe Warren, the main part of the mine being sited immediately south of Headland Warren farm (OS 100 NW). The mine was served by a cross-cut adit 287 fathoms in length which intersected six lodes. In 1848, levels driven 100 fathoms west and 150 fathoms east on South Lode were said to be yielding tin throughout. North Lode had been opened up at Shallow Adit for 100 fathoms east and 17 fathoms west from Engine Shaft which was then 12 fathoms below adit or 24 fathoms deep from surface. The bottom level extending 37 fathoms east and 52 west was producing more tin than at adit level. In 1856, twenty-seven heads of stamps were in use driven by two water-wheels. The pumps consisted of a bucket-lift operated by a 30ft wheel, the latter being connected to the shaft by three-quarters of a mile of flat rods.[87]

Due to financial difficulties, the mine was abandoned in 1851 but the company was soon reconstituted and the sett was amalgamated with Devon Great Tin Croft, which had started work some years earlier in adjoining ground on the east. The workings of the latter were originally confined to adit level, but during the next few years six shafts were sunk to a maximum depth of 24 fathoms. Despite the fact that some driving was done at this horizon, mainly by tributers, the results on the whole proved disappointing and in 1867 working ceased. In 1903 a fresh lease was acquired and operations continued intermittently and with diminishing success until 1926-7.[88]

Golden Dagger Mine (OS 99 NE), on the south of Birch Tor and Vitifer, lies close to the boundary of Manaton parish. The main workings were centered beneath the large open gunnises which extend across Soussons Down for a distance of over 1,000yd. Worked at intervals over a long period, the mine was noted for the very pure quality of its tin, and is said to have been actively developed in the period 1835–60.

In 1880 the sett was acquired by Moses Bawden, and in the course of the next four years £10,000 is claimed to have been spent in erecting machinery and treatment plant. Several new shafts were started at this time, among them Machine Shaft which was sunk to a depth of 40 fathoms. A long adit, to come in under the older workings, was also commenced in the lowest part of the valley.

In 1909 a new company was formed, and the Drainage Adit was extended to 1,250ft. The adit passed through 700–800ft of good tin ground from which one parcel of ore was sold at the rate of £131 per ton, then the best price for black tin for more than fifty years past. The mine was equipped at this time with a 16 head battery of Cornish stamps driven by a 22½ft by 9ft water-wheel, the pulp being concentrated on Wilfley tables capable of treating 35 tons a day.[89] In 1924 a turbo-generator and magnetic separator were introduced, but the latter appears to have been unsuccessful. Operations continued on a decreasing scale until the late 1920s. The mine now lies in a forestry plantation.

On the western side of the Moretonhampstead road, some 14½ miles from Tavistock, a lease was obtained in 1850 of an area of ground adjacent to the North Walla Brook. From the side of this an adit was started to connect with a proposed

Engine Shaft on the south-west. Through failure to obtain the necessary capital, the project was abandoned in 1852. In 1866 William Skewis, then agent at New Birch Tor and Vitifer Consols, renewed operations by sinking trial pits and trenches in the setts of Waterhill and Kings Oven.[90] Shortly after, Valley Shaft and Water Hill Shaft were started a short distance south of West Vitifer Mine (OS 99 NE).

In December 1869, the water being too quick to be kept by a horse-engine, it was proposed to bring in a leat from the North Walla Brook and to erect a pumping wheel. In the following year the property was acquired by a company formed in Bristol with a capital of £12,000. A 60ft wheel was erected at West Vitifer for stamping and pumping, and a number of promising lodes were opened up. In excavating the wheel-pit, old men's workings were revealed on the outcrop of the Black Pool Lode, samples of which showed values of up to £10 per fathom. In 1870 fourteen people were employed,[91] but three years later the authorised capital was exhausted. Although an additional £5,000 was raised, by 1875 this had also been spent and in that year the company was wound up, with no recorded production.[92]

Great Wheal Eleanor situated as shown on the OS map 90 SW about half a mile south-west of North Bovey village, was thought to lie on the most easterly extension of the Birch Tor and Vitifer run of lodes. The mine was restarted in 1875 by a local company when sampling showed fine-grained tin in payable quantities. On the strength of this a count-house and blacksmith's shop were erected, and soon after a 200hp engine with twenty-eight heads of stamps was purchased from Messrs Lanyon & Co of Truro. Water for dressing and other purposes was obtained from the boggy slopes of Easdon Down, and was fed into a pond immediately above the engine-shed.

The stamps were set to work in August 1876 when a commentator somewhat cautiously remarked, 'If they are able to keep all the buddles in full work (as from the enormous backs they have ready for stoping they seem likely to do) the returns of tin must be considerable.' In the following year the mine was inspected by Captain Josiah Thomas who reported that the lode in the 20 fathoms level contained 33lb of black tin to the ton. Engine Shaft was later deepened to 30 fathoms and was served by a shallow and deep adit, below which the water was drawn by a 6oft wheel. New Shaft, 9oyd west of Engine Shaft reached only to Deep Adit level, at this point 18 fathoms from surface. In 1880 the lode was said to be worth from 70 to 8olb of tin to the ton, and an additional eight heads of stamps were being prepared. In the following year, however, the mine was abandoned, the sole output of black tin recorded from 1876 amounting only to 20 tons.[93]

Little can be seen of the mine today other than a wheel-pit and, a short distance to the south-west, a fairly extensive open-cast working which appears to have been excavated by the old men on the back of another lode.

Page 109
(*above*) Birch Tor Mine, a view taken in the late 1920s; (*below*) buddle in workings at Vitifer mine

(*above*) All that remains of Wheal Julian, Plympton, a solitary stack
in a field. Immediately behind it can be seen the stack of Wheal
Sidney and in the further distance is the top of Bottle Hill Mine
stack; (*below*) the butt of the stack of the long-forgotten Cann Mine
near Plymbridge still survives despite widespread development all
round the area

PART THREE

YELVERTON TO PLYMOUTH

About one mile west of Yelverton station, prospecting trials were being carried out in 1853 at Devon Wheal Buller (OS 112 SW), where stones of yellow and black copper ore, 'all but solid copper', had been obtained from a shaft less than 2 fathoms deep. To the north of this spot, at Stoke Hill, costeaning (trenching or pitting) had revealed an east-west lode 2½ft wide, carrying tin ore, while at Cumerew a search was being made for other lodes near the southern boundary of the sett. An adit had been driven about 8 fathoms[1] and later in the year a horse-whim was erected.

Up to this time the work appears to have been financed by Sir Anthony Buller as a private venture, but in 1854 the mine was taken over by a cost-book company. By May of that year Emma's Engine Shaft had been sunk to 20 fathoms, and from it cross-cuts were being driven northwards. A year later a 36in steam engine was put to work, Engine Shaft being then 34 fathoms deep. The 20 level had been driven 50 fathoms east and a like distance west. Western Shaft was down to 10 fathoms. Production in 1855 amounted to 86 tons of copper ore,[2] the lode being reported as 3ft wide and yielding 2 tons of ore per fathom. In January 1859 a new shaft was being sunk, presumably the one later referred to as Down's. In June 1862 a 50in pumping engine was set to work, the ceremony being performed by Miss Emma Buller, daughter of Sir Anthony, 'who baptized it "Emma's engine" amidst the cheers of the miners and visitors . . .' By January 1863 Down's Shaft had been sunk to

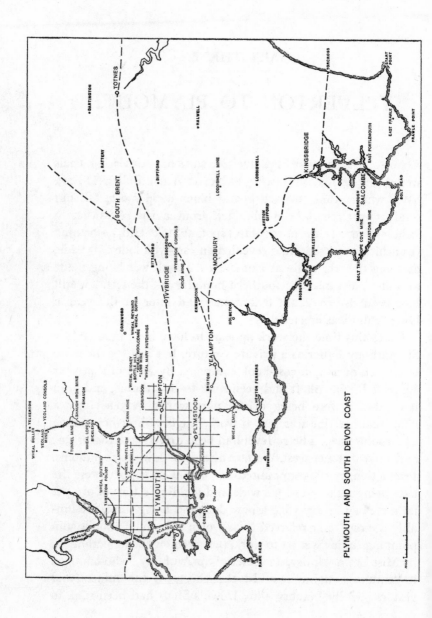

PLYMOUTH AND SOUTH DEVON COAST

65 fathoms from surface. The lode in the 55 fathom level, west, was about 3ft wide, composed of capels and peach (chlorite), while in the same level, east, it showed traces of black copper ore.[3]

Four months later the whole of the machinery and materials were put up for sale, these comprising Emma's Engine, a 10in rotary-whim, boilers, a horse-whim and about 70 fathoms of pit work. Phillips and Darlington record an output of 276 tons of copper ore in the year 1855-6,[4] whilst Dines gives a figure of 1,514 tons for the period 1855-61.

To the south of Yelverton, the area of Roborough Down is crossed by an estimated number of ten east–west lodes whose outcrop workings are visible today in the form of grass-grown entrenchments extending from Yeoland farm to the railway (OS 112 SW). Work was already in progress here in Elizabethan times, as appears from a letter by Sir Walter Raleigh to Sir Robert Cecil dated 15 November 1600: 'A gentleman, Mr Crymes, hath erected certain clash-mylls upon Roburghe Down to work the tynn which upon that place is gott with extreme labor and charge out of the ground. And because the townsmen of Plymouth seeke to procure all the commoditie thereabouts into their own hands, they allege that these mylls are prejudiciall to them and that the course of their water, which runneth through Plymouth, is diverted, contrary to a statute.'

In this conflict of interests, so familiar to mining companies of today, Sir Walter came down firmly on the side of the miners. 'I took paines,' he continues, 'to view the river [Meavy] and mylls. I found that in my opinion they [Plymouth] could not disallow the using or the building of the same for that there are about 200 works which must be unwrought without the use of such clash-mylls and benefit of that river.' The Plymouth townsfolk, however, were not willing to let the matter rest there: 'They have procured sub penas out of the Starre Chamber to call the matter in question – the matter being tryable and determinable in the Stannary Court where it now dependeth.

But if this be suffered to proceed in the Starre Chamber it will not be available to speak of Her Majesty's ... encrease of custom or to establish good lawes amongst the Tynners, when others who can by a great purse, or procuring extraordinary means, diminish ... her Majesty's duties and the common benefytt of the people.'[5]

Although it is reasonable to suppose that the lodes were developed by adits and shafts at an early period, there are no known records to confirm this. An old but undated plan, referred to by Dines, shows a Shallow and a Deep Adit (the portal of the latter opening on the west bank of the Meavy, opposite Olderwood farm), whence it connected to the Engine Shaft of Yeoland Consols (marked on the OS map 112 SW as Yeoland Mine). In 1853 the depth of this mine was stated to be 64 fathoms from surface, with levels driven east and west at 30, 42, 54 and 64 fathoms, all of which had proved productive particularly the 42 and 54. The lode was of great size, '8 to 10 fathoms wide in places'. A new perpendicular shaft was then being sunk, which at 22 fathoms from surface would pass through the North Lode which was expected in depth to prove as productive as the Main Lode on which operations were then being conducted.[6]

By 1856 Engine Shaft had been sunk to 74 fathoms from surface on the course of the lode. There was a 36in steam engine driving twenty-four heads of stamps in addition to pumping, and a 22in engine served for hoisting. Since the commencement of operations in 1851, sales of black tin had realised £13,000, the latest quarterly returns amounting to 15 tons. Production was expected to increase as two new levels were then being opened out in good ground at 56 fathoms below adit. It was also intended to deepen the shaft,[7] but in March 1857 it was decided to abandon operations, and the mine and materials were put up for sale.

East Yeoland, which lay below the railway adjacent to the dressing-floors of Yeoland Consols, was by comparison only lightly developed, apart from a small winze there being no workings below the Deep Adit level. In 1853 the manager reported that a cross-cut had been driven 6 fathoms south from the adit intersecting a lode 9ft wide containing good work for tin.[8] There appears, however, to have been no production.

On Chubbtor Farm, a short distance south of East Yeoland, Plymouth Wheal Yeoland developed three lodes. A report on this property in 1848 by Charles Thomas, manager of Dolcoath Mine, states that on North Lode an adit had been driven for 100 fathoms, at a depth of 10 to 14 fathoms below surface. About £10 worth of tin had been raised from this level, but the appearances on the whole were 'exceedingly poor'. On South Lode, a shaft had been sunk 23 fathoms and an engine erected. The 12 fathom level extended 24 fathoms, and at one point had returned some tin; but the end of the lode was unproductive. The 24 fathom level passed beneath this tin ground, but was of value only for about 5 fathoms. New South Lode near the Engine Shaft had been worked for 10 or 12 fathoms, at a maximum depth of 5 fathoms from surface. Over a short length the lode was worth about £4 per fathom. In concluding his report the writer suggested sinking the shaft to 30 fathoms and driving on the South Lode at the 20 where it was about 2ft wide and not unpromising in character.[9]

In 1855, by which time the name of the mine had been changed to South Yeoland, a 32in engine and twelve heads of stamps had been erected and the shaft sunk vertically to 33 fathoms. Cross-cuts had been put out north and south to intersect parallel lodes. Some tin had been sold, but the workings at this time were principally for copper,[10] of which Smith's Shop Lode had returned ore assaying 27 per cent metal from one bunch. Despite this, operations were abandoned shortly after, the sett and machinery being advertised for sale in August 1855 (*Mining Journal*).

It would appear from outcrop workings that the Yeoland lodes were formerly pursued for a considerable distance to the east. In 1886 Captain Joel Manley of Horrabridge stated in *Mining Journal* (28 August) that at 'Elderwood [Olderwood as shown on the map] we are putting down a shaft through old men's workings and at a depth of about 7 fathoms are finding parts of the lode producing 200 lbs. of black tin to the ton of stuff'.

In 1881 a new company was formed, entitled Yeoland Consols, with a capital of £60,000 – £20,000 of which was pocketed by the promoters. The project called forth an embittered letter from the former manager, Captain Richard Williams, whose opinion of the mine was summed up in his final words 'the lode is large, the ground bad and the average yield of black tin does not exceed 4 lbs. per ton. To say that the lode improved in depth is not true'. On the face of it, the fortunes of the company justified this condemnation. A first batch of concentrate, amounting only to 16cwt, was sent to the Redruth Tin Smelting Company in August 1883. It was stated at this time that 2,000 tons of tinstuff were ready for stamping, but no machinery had been erected nor had any arrangements been made for bringing in water to dress it.

In 1884, two years after operations had started, the mine was still without water or steam-power and no development had been carried out other than lengthening an adit by 20 fathoms and walling up the sides of a wheel-pit. Due to a prolonged drought, the mine was again short of water in 1886, although 36 tons of concentrate had been sold in the first seven months of that year. A promise had been made of additional capital for sinking a shaft, but in 1887 the directors reported that this had failed to materialise. Working at that time was still confined to above the adit level, and by the end of the year the funds of the company were virtually exhausted. A proposal to form a new company in 1888 came to nothing, and by 1890 the shares had ceased to be quoted.[11] It is clear that this last working was a costly failure, but whether primarily due to the incompetence of the directors in all matters relating to mining, or to poverty of the lodes it is impossible to say since the latter were never seen in depth.

THE BICKLEIGH AND PLYMPTON NEIGHBOURHOOD

About 1858 a copper lode was discovered in the parish of Bickleigh when the Leebeer Tunnel (OS 112 SW) on the Plymouth to Tavistock Railway was being driven. In the roof of the tunnel, about 66ft below surface, the lode was fully 4ft wide showing 'stones of rich horseflesh copper ore and green carbonate, the north part of the lode for a foot wide being almost as green as a leek'. Near the floor of the tunnel, however, the lode contracted to one foot 'very hard, no ore and but little greens to be seen'. The enclosing rock was an exceedingly hard granite. In 1859 a prospectus was issued under the heading of the Tunnel Mine, a name which was altered in the following year to Bickleigh Vale Phoenix. The copper lode was stated at this time to be 12ft wide where it had been opened at surface, while a tin lode 4 to 6ft in width had recently been found near the tunnel's mouth. Abundant water was available from the river which ran close by, and a good road passed through the property to the 'copper quay'. Despite these attractions, it appears that the company failed to interest the investing public, and beyond driving a short adit, little work was done and in 1862 operations were suspended.[12]

In Vicarage Wood and Hele Bottom (OS 118 NW), some three-quarters of a mile north-west of Bickleigh Church, two lodes carrying copper, blende (zinc ore) and small amounts of tin strike east–west across a north–south valley. These were exploited in a mine called Wheal Lopes (or Lopez), a lease for which is said to have been granted by the Lopes family in 1760. However, the earliest working of which any particulars are known took place in the second decade of the last century. By 1821 the Main Lode had been explored for 120 fathoms west and 60 fathoms east by an adit. Below this, the 10 fathom level extended 5 fathoms east and 20 fathoms west; and the 14 fathom level extended 15 fathoms east and 65 fathoms west. In this last, the lode yielded 140 tons of good copper ore. The bottom level (24 fathoms below adit), was driven 7 and 50 fathoms east and west respectively, and also contained ore of 'superior quality'. South Lode (40 fathoms south of Main Lode) returned a few tons of yellow copper ore at the Adit Level (here about 7 fathoms below surface).

As shown on the OS map, water to drive the machinery was brought to the mine by a long leat from the Plym, an expensive undertaking which involved tunnelling through 500 feet of hard granite at the intake from the river. In 1823 the sett and materials were put up for sale, the latter comprising a 30ft water-wheel, horse-whims and a stamping mill. The mine was described as being near Jump (now known as Roborough), within four miles of Lophill (Lopwell) Quay, and five from Plymouth Dock (Devonport).[13] Subsequent to its closure, 26 tons of copper ore were sold in 1825.

About 1840 the sett was acquired by the Plymouth and Dartmoor Mining Company, and two 40ft water-wheels were installed, together with a new drawing machine. During the spring of 1844 work was proceeding in the 30, 50 and 60 fathom levels, and returns were averaging 20 tons per month. In May of that year *Mining Journal* reported that the mine was also producing copper precipitate at the rate of several hundred-weight a month, and that the copper ore raised during this working had totalled 552 tons which realised £2,666. Most of the ore had come from the western part of the mine. The main shaft was then down to 82 and another shaft to 62 fathoms below adit. Owing to the fall in the standard of copper from £107 to £90, working ceased at the end of 1844, the materials being auctioned in March 1846. The sett was taken up again in January 1856 when the standard had risen to £130 In addition, a great quantity of blende, which had been laid open in the previous working when that mineral was almost value-less, was now worth £3 a ton, so that profits were anticipated. A new 40ft wheel, 8 feet in the breast, was erected together with other machinery, but owing to mismanagement and various financial difficulties the lower levels were never forked (pumped out).[14]

In 1860 the plant was still standing on the property and ready to work again 'at a week's notice'. An attempt to sell the mine in 1862 failed to obtain a purchaser, but at length in 1865 a company was formed, under dubious auspices, and as Devon Wheal Lopes working was resumed. In the course of the next two years the leat and adit were cleared, the 40ft wheel rehabilitated, and the Engine Shaft forked to the 62 fathom level. But the shareholders were not happy, and com-plaints were frequent regarding the misappropriation of capital and the unscrupulous character of some of the directors. Operations continued for a short time longer, but by 1868 the mine had closed and the company was being wound up.[15]

Until the early 1960s, the shaft in Vicarage Wood was open to the adit, and on the eastern bank of the stream the wheel-pit, with ruined buildings adjoining, was still visible. However, the area had already been planted with young conifers, and these have since obscured the last traces of its mining past.

Near the east bank of the Plym, south of Shaugh Bridge, a vertical north-south iron lode has been worked in a sheer-sided open-cut in Square's Wood (OS 118 NW). The excavation was drained by an adit, with a communicating shaft, brought up from the west, and in the four years prior to 1838 operations were carried on by Messrs Langdon & Paddon of Stonehouse. The ore was said to be intermixed with plumbago (black lead), and there were 'indications' of a copper vein crossing the iron lode, the former supposed to be an extension of one of the Wheal Lopes lodes. By 1840 a leat had been brought in from the River

Cad,[16] and a water-wheel erected with flat-rods and pumps. Parallel with the Square's Wood Lode, about 50yd to the east, a long narrow quarry is shown on the map adjacent to the road to Shaugh Prior. Iron stone has also been found here.[17]

In 1859 the Shaugh Iron Mine was advertised for sale; numerous enquiries were received, but there were no takers owing to the exorbitant dues of 2s 6d a ton demanded by the mineral lord, Sir Massey Lopes. The mine was subsequently worked during the short-lived iron boom of the 1870s, when an output of 4,670 tons was recorded.[18] Some further examination of the deposit was carried out by a Mr Ward in 1938, but the ore was found to be too much contaminated by arsenic to justify working.

A short distance north of Plym Bridge (OS 118 SW), the small Cann Mine was worked about 1824–5 by Messrs Petherick of St Blazey, Cornwall. The lode was originally cut when excavating the canal which served the Cann Slate Quarry, and for this reason the venture was otherwise known as the Canal Mine. In 1829 the sett was regranted to Joseph Thomas Austen, the well-known Cornish industrialist who later assumed the name of Treffry. A surface plan prepared in that year[19] shows three shafts, one on the west bank of the canal adjoining the river, the others just east of the canal The mine is said to have been drained by a branch of the Boringdon Mine adit, and was later developed by a steam engine 'the remains of which and the old burrows can now be seen', as a correspondent of *Mining Journal* pointed out in December 1859. More remarkably, traces of the little engine-house still remained in 1956, having just escaped obliteration by the embankment of the Plymouth–Tavistock Railway, at the foot of which it stands. Nothing else is known of this virtually forgotten mine which receives no mention by Collins or Dines.

East of Plym Bridge, Boringdon Park Mine (OS 118 SW) has been worked on at least three occasions. About 1820 a certain Captain Remfry started operations on a lead lode exposed on the edge of the wood, some three-quarters of a mile west-north-west of Boringdon Manor. From here an adit was driven 200 fathoms on the course of the lode, but owing to the flatness of the ground was nowhere more than 12 fathoms below surface. Working continued until 1824 when the sett and materials, including a 23ft water-wheel, were advertised for sale.[20] Ten years later the mine was taken up by a Captain Bray, soon after which a company was formed. In the autumn of 1836 a 30in steam engine, designed by William West, was ordered from the Hayle Foundry in Cornwall, its shipment to the mine being considerably delayed by the storminess of the weather. Some rich parcels of silver-lead ore and a quantity of black jack (zinc ore) were returned during this working which ended in 1839, mainly through lack of power in the engine to cope with the water when the shaft reached a depth of 50 fathoms from surface.[21]

About 700ft to the east, East Boringdon Mine developed an extension of the same lode. To unwater this, the Boringdon Park adit was extended to a total length of nearly three-quarters of a mile, entering East Boringdon Shaft at a depth of 32 fathoms from surface. Meanwhile, work had restarted at Boringdon Park Mine, and in 1852 the two setts were united and became known as Boringdon Consols. A new 40in cylinder pumping engine was erected on the Boringdon Shaft, whence by means of flat-rods it also drew the water from East Boringdon. In the course of the next few years, Murchison's or Engine Shaft was sunk to 40 fathoms, Hitchin's to 35 fathoms, and Annie's Engine Shaft was deepened to 72 fathoms from surface. The East Mine was eventually developed to a 48 fathom level below adit, and in the Old Mine there were levels below adit at 15, 30 and 40 fathoms.[22]

Records of output from 1852–7 comprised 400 tons of lead ore, 10 tons of blende, about 8,000oz of silver (Dines, p 686), and an unspecified amount of copper ore. The final sale of the materials took place in February 1857 and included the engine, a 38ft diameter water-wheel for crushing and several horse-whims. Summing up its history in December 1859, *Mining Journal* remarked that the stoppage of the mine resulted more from financial embarrassment than impoverishment of the lodes and that there was a probability of its being worked again.

Adjoining Boringdon Consols on the north, and separated only 'by the drive through Boringdon Wood called the Forty Foot Ride', Wheal Harriet Sophia was said to lie on a westward continuation of the Wheal Sidney lodes. The sett had been only slightly worked, but in 1859 'the Sidney party were said to be taking it up as their levels were approaching the boundary'.[23]

Through Fernhill Wood a line of old surface workings coursing east-west marks the outcrop of the lodes of Wheal Sidney (OS 118 SE), its name derived from the mineral owner, Sidney Strode of Newnham Park. The sett extends from the Tory Brook on the east to a point just west of the road running north from Plympton to Cadover Bridge, and contains three lodes yielding tin and arsenic. When reopened in 1850, the mine was said to have been 'supposedly worked over 300 years since'. Although little is known of its early history beyond the fact that it was active in 1795,[24] the outcrop workings are probably far older than this and might indeed be almost of any age. At the time of its restarting, the shaft was already down to 90 fathoms on the underlie and was served by a Shallow Adit brought up by the old men from the Elfordleigh valley on the south-west, the adit entering the shaft at some 12 fathoms below surface.[25] Deep Adit is driven into the sett from the Tory Brook Valley, and near its mouth lay the dressing-floors which were connected to the shafts by a tramway through the wood. In 1854 there were twenty-four heads of stamps in operation, and 100 tons of black tin had been sold in the two previous years at prices varying from £65 to £82 per ton. By 1855 the mine had about broken even, the value of sales to that date having amounted to £8,459 on a called-up capital of £8,832.[26]

Some time before 1860 a new shaft was started 100 fathoms

north of the old mine with a view to taking the lode in its northerly dip. The workings were drained by a 45ft water-wheel situated on the west bank of the Tory Brook and connected to the pumps by wooden flat-rods over a quarter of a mile in length. On reaching a depth of 65 fathoms, a stream of water was cut in the shaft bottom, which drowned the pumps and inundated the mine. However, this setback was soon overcome. Within a few months the shaft was re-equipped with 15 and 16in plungers, and the old flat-rods, which had been subject to constant breakages, were replaced by new 2½in rods with hammered-iron joints – enabling the shaft to be sunk to its ultimate depth of 100 fathoms. By means of cross-cuts, a large amount of tin ground was opened up, although the mine still laboured under the disadvantages of being worked solely by underhand stopes and having only a crab winch for hoisting the ore.[27] Between 1854 and 1864 sales of 412 tons of black tin were recorded, part of which may have come from Wheal Julian, which stands about 300yd north of Wheal Sidney and developed parallel lodes.

In 1855 the Wheal Julian sett was acquired by Messrs H. D. Skewis of Beeralston and John Sims of Calstock, who initiated trials in the old men's workings. A gunnis 3 to 4 fathoms wide was opened up in which oak trees believed to be over 200 years old were standing – proof that nothing had been done there 'since the work of the ancients'. Tin worth £65 to £70 a ton was found in some of the old pillars (arches), and numerous veins were also visible on the northern side of the gunnis. Near this a small shaft was sunk to take the lode at a depth of 20 fathoms. In the south part of the gunnis, some 70 fathoms east of the shaft, the lode was 3ft wide and worth 'at least' £100 per fathom.[28]

After a lapse of two or three years, occasioned by the exorbitant terms and unreasonable restrictions imposed by the mineral owner, Mr Julian of Laira House, Plymouth, working was renewed on a somewhat larger scale. At the bottom of the trial shaft a cross-cut was put out to the South Lode and on this a level producing rich stones of tin was driven 8 or 10 fathoms. A 22in steam engine was installed in 1857, and in the following year South Lode was reported to be 7 to 8ft wide in the 18 fathom level and carrying tin, peach (chlorite) and gossan worth £30 to £40 per fathom. However, due to the lack of water for dressing and other purposes and the difficulty of acquiring rights over certain adjoining fields, the materials were offered for sale in April 1859 and in the following January the sett was advertised to let with immediate possession. Working was resumed in that year, the water being drawn out by a small 18in 'double-engine' acquired from North Tamar Mine.[29] According to the plan, Engine Shaft was eventually sunk to 60 fathoms, where a cross-cut south from the bottom intersected the Main Lode at a distance of 58 fathoms. Although worked until 1860 as separate mines, Wheal Julian was subsequently amalgamated with Wheal Sidney, and in 1865 the machinery of the combined sett consisted of a 56in pumping engine and a 18in winding engine, together with two 45ft water-wheels. Operations appear to have continued into the 1880s, a section of the Main Lode accompanying the plan being dated 1882.[30]

Eastward of Wheal Sidney a number of mines, mostly small, have been worked along the course of the Smallhanger Brook. The more southerly of these was Hemerdon Consols (OS 118 SE),[31] which included the Lobb Mine on the farm of that name. About 1820 an adit had been driven there on a promising tin lode, but since it adjoined Mr Strode's game preserves no grant could be obtained and the trial was abandoned. The southern portion of Hemerdon Consols was started or restarted in 1851 when a shaft was sunk to 40 fathoms by means of a 32in William West rotary engine which served for pumping, hoisting and stamping. The upper levels showed good values, but the productiveness of the lodes is said to have diminished in depth where they entered the hard granite. Some thousands of pounds were spent, and about £1,200 worth of black tin recovered prior to the mine being abandoned in 1856.[32]

Ten years later, working was resumed in the western part of the same sett under the name of Wheal Mary Hutchings. By October 1868 more than £5,000 worth of tin had been returned from a depth of only 20 fathoms, and 'hundreds of fathoms of tin ground had been laid open'. During the same month a new pumping wheel 50ft in diameter, 6ft breast, was set to work, being christened 'Medlycott' by Mrs Strode, wife of the mineral owner. Water from this was carried on to a second wheel, 45ft in diameter, which drove twenty-four heads of stamps. In the year ended November 1868, sales of 53 tons of black tin were recorded, and in 1873 the mine was 52 fathoms deep from surface and employed 105 people. Between 1866 and 1880 sales amounted to 426 tons of black tin, 221 tons of mispickel, and 230 tons of arsenic.[33]

Near the 500ft contour between the valleys of the Small-hanger Brook and the Tory Brook, the stack of Bottle Hill Mine (OS 118 SE) forms a conspicuous feature of the landscape. Among the most extensively developed of all the mines in this area, it also possesses one of the longest recorded histories. On 24 June 1715, a new lease of the sett was granted by Sidney Strode of Newnham to John Long of Tavistock, bookseller, and James Mager, tinner, of Plympton St Mary. The latter, it was stated, 'on making an essay to dig delve and search for tin within the tin work or mine known by the name of Bottle Hill, situate . . . in the Bowling Green there', had discovered a copper lode adjoining the tin lode. Liberty was afforded to work this for 40 fathoms in length and 5 fathoms in breadth on the course of the lode 'that is to say fifteen fathoms in length to the westward of the west shaft that is now on the said work and 25 fathoms to the east of the said shaft'. The 'dish' or royalty was fixed at one-ninth; the division of ore to be made once a month 'or as often as twenty tons shall be raised and made merchantable'.[34] This appears to be the earliest instance of copper being found at Bottle Hill, but it is clear from the reference to existing shafts that the tin lodes had been developed by underground mining long before 1715.

In a later working from 1811 to 1846, the sett was described as a mile long on the course of the lodes, of which there were four. A deep adit brought up from the Tory Brook unwatered these to 60 fathoms in the higher ground, where the Engine Shaft was sunk 110 fathoms from surface. Tin and copper ores to the value of £100,000 were raised during this working, which was abandoned when good returns were still being made. The water-wheel, however, had broken down and most of the machinery being in a bad state, the adventurers were unwilling to put up the money for replacements in the then depressed state of the tin market.

In 1850 a new company was formed and in June of that year the committee reported that the lode in the 12 fathom level, west, was 5 to 6ft wide and worth £100 per fathom. In the 24 level the lode was of similar width, carrying tin and copper ores. Eight shafts had been sunk, of which five extended to the 40 fathom level and three to the 110. A 50in cylinder engine was erected at this time, together with five water-wheels, and thirty-six heads of stamps were in operation. However, in April 1853 the manager reported that he was unable to develop the property in a miner-like way through lack of funds, and two years later the sett was abandoned and the machinery advertised for sale.[35] Working was resumed in 1860, and the mine continued in operation until 1882 when the Engine Shaft reached a depth of 130 fathoms from surface, or 70 fathoms below adit. Subsequently, however, little or no work was done below that level, and it would seem that future prospects for the mine must lie in deeper development of the ore shoots above or within the underlying granite.[36]

At Drakeland on the eastern side of the Smallhanger Brook (OS 118 SE), Wheal Woolcombe, or East Bottle Hill, lay near the granite-killas contact at the northen foot of Hemerdon Ball.

Page 127
Deeply wreathed in ivy, this engine-house, dating from the 1850s, is almost all that remains of the surface of Ivybridge Consols Lead and Silver Mine

The stack working the end of the long underground arsenic flue
at Wheal Sidney, Plympton. These working are buried in deep
woodland

The sett contained the Bucking House and New South Lodes of old Bottle Hill, but did not include the Main or the New North Lodes of the latter mine. Under the title of East Bottle Hill, operations commenced in 1862 when an adit was driven into the rising ground, intersecting first a copper and then a tin lode. The outcrop of the latter had been extensively worked by the old men and was cut in the adit at 30 fathoms from surface. A shaft was also sunk on this lode, which was said to be rich. In 1867 a 6oft diameter water-wheel was erected for driving the stamps, and also to serve for pumping and winding. Spargo (1868) gives the depths of the workings as 24 fathoms, adding that although no sales had been recorded 'hopes were entertained of future profit'. Sixteen people were employed in 1870, and the mine was still on the active list in 1873.[37]

North of Bottle Hill Mine, on Crownhill Down, a shaft with a number of old entrenchments mark the site of a mine known locally as Whiteworks. Here the backs of at least two lodes had been worked by the old men in bygone days, both by streaming and mining. In 1846, under the name of Wheal Albert, the sett was taken up by a group of working miners. 'In resuming the work of the ancients', several rich branches of pure-grain tin were discovered at a depth of 11 fathoms, underlying north. On one of these a shaft was sunk to a depth of 26 fathoms, the water being drawn by a 20ft wheel, whilst a 12ft wheel drove three heads of stamps. The ore required only the lightest possible crushing, 'Indeed,' as the captain reported, 'most of it may be washed without stamping at all, the ground being a soft decomposed granite and china clay.' About two tons of tin concentrates were prepared for sale, but on driving the 25 fathom level they holed into old men's workings. This proved so discouraging that the sett was abandoned after a trial of eighteen months. In 1859 the property was acquired by another party and entitled Wheal Florence, the name which appears on the OS map (118 SE). In December of that year the sett was being 'only slightly worked'.[38]

Near Baccamore Pits (OS 118 SE), one mile east of Hemerdon Ball, work was in progress in 1846 at a little mine called Wheal Reynard (or Renard), where a shallow adit driven north about 70 fathoms intersected a copper and a tin lode. The latter was said to be 2ft wide and yielded fair values, although only 60ft below surface. At this depth a level was extended for 20 fathoms and the lode thought worthy of further trial, but the owner of the adjoining land refused to permit the work and it was abandoned.[39]

Further to the east a 10ft wide lode composed of gossan, peach (chlorite), mundic and spots of copper ore was opened up in 1853 in a pit sunk at Wheal Sophia. In the hope of attracting investors, specimens of the ore were displayed at Cornwood Station which lay within the sett.[40] Apparently they failed to do so. Near the station a promising copper lode was reported to lie beneath the lawn of Blatchford House on the Yealm. Sir John Rogers, the owner of the estate, allowed some trials to be made, but permission was subsequently withdrawn by his widow.

LEAD, SILVER AND IRON AROUND PLYMOUTH

In 1849 during excavations for a new road northward from Crownhill to join the Tamerton Foliot road, a north-south lead lode was discovered about half a mile east of Whitleigh Hall (OS 117 SE). Under the name of Wheal Gennys, a shaft was started on 9 January 1950, the ceremony of cutting the first sod being performed by Mrs Gennys, wife of the owner of the Whitleigh estate. Six months later the shaft was down to 19 fathoms and on reaching the depth of 25 fathoms it was intended to cross-cut to the lode. The amount of water at this time was trifling and was bailed by a horse-whim, but a 36in cylinder steam engine had been erected for use when needed. The engine-house was of unusual design with a flat roof 'from the top of which is a delightful view of the Hamoaze'. At the 32 fathom level, 26 fathoms south from the shaft, the stopes yielded 6cwt of ore per fathom. In the 42 fathom level similar values obtained, the lode being 5ft wide in places. Sinking was continued to a depth of 52 fathoms, soon after which the shaft 'fell together' and in a mood of panic the mine was abandoned.[41]

A year or two later, working was resumed as Wheal Whitleigh, and in 1854 45 tons of argentiferous lead ore was sold for £870. By the end of that year the shaft had been made secure and deepened to 72 fathoms. In the 62 fathom level a rich course of silver-lead was encountered, 30 fathoms in length. This was intersected again by a cross-cut at the 72 where it showed an improvement on the level above. Driving was then in progress north and south at that horizon, and by May 1855 Engine Shaft reached its ultimate depth of 82 fathoms where another cross-cut was started to the lode. Soon after this, for what reason it is not clear, the mine was stopped and the 36in engine with the rest of the materials was offered for sale – leaving two engine-houses standing on the property. Output during this last working is recorded as 62 tons of lead ore and 1,436oz of silver.[42] In 1958 traces of the mine were still visible at Zoar Cottages (OS 117 SE provisional edition), on the fringe of one of the new housing estates of post-war Plymouth. These remains consisted of two small dumps in the gardens adjoining the road-cutting, 1,000yd north-west of the Crownhill junction. The cottages themselves (since demolished) had the appearance of having formerly been the mine count-house. When the Tamerton Foliot road was widened in 1973, traces of the lead lode in soft clay were exposed in a side-cutting which has since been walled in.

In September 1859 readers of *Mining Journal* were informed that 'Near Knackersknowle village [now Crownhill] a little mine is working called the Devonshire Silver-Lead Mine from which some splendid specimens of silver-lead ore have been produced. The sett extends north and south of the turnpike road and the southern part was worked as Wheal Gennys and was abandoned some years since . . . Operations are now being conducted on the north part of the sett and include a cross-cut adit driven 60 fathoms, with a trial shaft 5 fathoms deep.' In the following year the adit intersected an east-west lode consisting of white iron, with a leader of argentiferous ore assaying 337 oz of silver to the ton. However, the captain stated that in continuing the adit north the ground was becoming harder and the lode had split. By November 1859 about 97 fathoms of development, including 50 fathoms of cross-cuts, had been carried out at a depth of a little more than 4 fathoms. A further 16 fathoms had been tested by surface shoding. All work appears to have ceased by July 1860[43] with no recorded production.

The discoveries originally made at Wheal Whitleigh gave rise to a number of other trials in the same area. On 27 March 1850 work was started at Wheal Langmaid where there were said to be two lodes lying immediately north of the Whitleigh sett. An open cutting was brought up on one of these, where the back of the lode was over 5ft wide and showing traces of lead ore impregnated with silver. On this a shaft was sunk to 26 fathoms and a cross-cut put out to the lodes which were believed to form a junction at that depth. A level was then driven north through ground consisting of flookan (soft clay) in which cubes of lead were visible. The venture was claimed by its promoters to be a 'model mine', and it certainly boasted one strange innovation. As a shareholder of the concern wrote to *Mining Journal* in June 1851, 'If any of your readers had been travelling on the Tamerton–Plymouth road in February last, they would have feasted their eyes with a new spectacle – namely a water-wheel turned by human power or treadmill fashion which as one of the "convicts" told me, made him sore all over at the end of the day.'

During the same month a Captain Lean was asked to report on the property. In this he stated that the bottom level had a slate-coloured flookan 1ft wide running north-south and dipping west 2ft in a fathom. Twenty-nine fathoms had been driven north and the flookan presented the same character throughout: 'a few specks of lead but not a lead lode'. In the level above, the same results attended the driving. Captain Lean's conclusion was that a cross-cut should be put out west 'and if nothing better is discovered than what you have been driving on, the sooner you wind up the concern the better, for to go on thus is nothing but a wilful waste of money which you will never see back if you wait till Doomsday'.[44] In the face of these disparaging remarks it was decided to abandon the mine, the 20ft wheel or 'treadmill' being sold soon after.

Some years earlier two east-west lodes had been prospected by an adit in an adjoining sett named Wheal Looseleigh. In driving north a branch of copper ore 4ft wide was intersected at 38 fathoms from the mouth of the adit, which was continued to an ultimate length of 64 fathoms. Here it cut into a large 'dropper' believed to be part of the North Lode. The latter had a steep underlay and was thought to unite with the South Lode in depth. In addition to copper, the lodes carried small amounts of lead, black jack (zinc ore) and fluorspar.[45] Although little else has been recorded of this mine, traces of a shaft were still visible in 1958 on the housing estate due north of Looseleigh, and a second shaft was formerly to be seen near the altitude figure 364 in Southway Lane, east of Tamerton Foliot (OS 117 SE). It is impossible to say whether these shafts were sunk by the Looseleigh adventurers or by a company called Wheal Southway which was formed in 1857,[46] since no particulars of the latter are known.

There can be no doubt that mineral deposits exist beneath the streets of Plymouth. Within recent years, iron ore has been found on an industrial site in George Street, Stonehouse, and about 1958 traces of copper were discovered near Eldad Hill. The name Copper Place is commonly thought to commemorate a deposit of ore, but may equally refer to a former copper regulus works in this neighbourhood. In 1850, when the foundations for the new prison (now the Plymouth Police Headquarters) were being excavated, a copper lode was revealed crossing the old Tavistock turnpike road at North Hill.[47] There is no evidence of any of these mineral finds being worked.

In contrast to this, limestone was extensively developed and there is little doubt that the now 'lost' caves of Stonehouse were subterranean quarries which were active in the eighteenth century and possibly very much earlier.[48]

During the last century at least two mines were in existence on the shores of the Cattewater. The earlier of these was the Wheal Morley Iron Ore and Clay Works which was started in 1839. In 1841 it was stated that about 600 tons of good quality iron ore was then standing on the quays. The clay was taken out in 'open heads' and proved equally suitable for potting and brickmaking. Several thousand tons of this clay were awaiting sale on the premises.[49]

In 1877 the sale was advertised of the Turnchapel Iron Mine on the Cattewater. Here a shaft had been sunk about 7 fathoms deep, 100yd from the quay, and opening up a lode 7ft in width from which 40 to 50 tons had been 'brought to grass' (surface). The ore consisted of a brown haematite yielding 57 per cent of metallic iron, with an almost complete absence of phosphorus. The plant comprised a 14hp steam engine, 8 ton Cornish boiler, together with the necessary drying sheds.[50]

THE YEALM AND ERME VALLEYS, AND THE SOUTH HAMS

East of Plymouth a number of widely scattered ore deposits have been worked or prospected in the coastal belt between the A38 road and the sea. On the Courtgate estate in Plymstock, work was restarted in 1857 at Pollexfen Consols, under a grant from the Bastard family of Kitley House. In December of that year an adit capable of giving 20 fathoms of backs was being driven into a hill towards a promising copper lode. At a depth of only 8ft from surface the lode was 5ft in width and composed of yellow ore and pyrite. A shaft was then sinking through old men's workings which extended to a depth of 32ft. Below this a level was driven south for 5 fathoms, but here the lode was only 18in wide. In the following year a north-south lead-course was encountered assaying 60 per cent lead and 25 to 400z of silver to the ton. Soon afterwards the lack of pumping facilities prevented further exploration.[51] The mine derived its name from the Pollexfens who were resident at Kitley in the reign of Henry VIII. In 1710 the property passed by marriage to the Bastard family in whose possession it still remains (W. G. Hoskins, *Devon*, 1972 ed, p 520).

On the west bank of the River Yealm, just south of its junction with Cofflete Creek, Wheal Emily (OS 130 NE) was notable for the presence of antimony in association with silver-lead. Following an earlier working, the mine was reopened in 1849 when the development consisted of sinking a vertical shaft and driving two adits. The shaft is situated in a piece of rough ground bordering the south side of Wembury Wood, about 200ft above river level. Shallow Adit lies in the steep wooded slopes below and was driven 35 fathoms south-west where it meets the lode which it then follows 5 fathoms south-east and 20 fathoms north-west, passing the shaft on the north-east side. Some small heaps of ore near the mouth of this adit were examined by the late Sir Arthur Russell, Bt, in 1949 and yielded jamesonite with pyrite and quartz, together with a small quantity of bournonite and galena.[52] Deep Adit's portal adjoins the letter W of HWMO Tides as shown on the 6in map and was driven 355 fathoms (2,130ft), no small achievement prior to the introduction of the compressed-air rock-drill.

In 1849 assays of the ore in the 12 fathom level gave a produce of 45, 80 and 110oz of silver to the ton. A winze sunk below this level showed a branch of solid lead ore 1ft wide which was opened up for a length of 24 fathoms. In this the assay value of the silver was said to have been as high as 375oz. Five assays made in the following year by Captain W. Knott of Wheal Langford, gave a more conservative view of the silver values, the produce of these being 14, 16, 24, 30 and 53oz per ton. A single stone of antimony selected from the dressing-floors yielded 19oz to the ton. The shaft at this time was only 17 fathoms deep and the intention was to continue it down to the 35 fathom or Deep Adit level 'at the mouth of which a vessel of 200 tons burden may anchor with perfect safety'.[53] In fact, this communication was not made since according to plan, the Deep Adit level passes south-west of the shaft.[54] A new manager was appointed in April 1850 when further rich silver ores were discovered and the deep adit was cleared. Working ceased before 1852, as a consequence, it is said, of quarrelling and litigation among the adventurers.

In contrast to many equally small mines, Wheal Emily has passed almost unnoticed in the mining literature of the last 100 years, and today its existence is largely unknown even to local people. That this is so can only be explained by its isolated position and the concealment of the workings in the precipitous wooded countryside in which they lie.

Wheal Francis, in the valley of the Erme near Ivybridge, was a small silver-lead mine, the sole knowledge of which is derived from a prospectus,[55] undated but by the watermark of the paper judged to be c1820. The mine was stated to have been worked 102 years earlier than this when, despite the lack of any machinery, it had given large returns from a shallow depth. At the time when the prospectus was issued, an adit was being driven into the hillside on the opposite side of the river from the older working and due to the steepness of the ground the adit end was already 17 fathoms below surface. The lode at that point was 20in wide and becoming richer as the work advanced. Eight or ten tons of ore had already been recovered, giving assay values of 14 in 20 of lead and 40oz of silver to the ton.

Below the adit a copper lode had been found, showing rich stones of green ore (malachite). It was intended to explore this to a depth of 12 fathoms. The expense of bringing the little mine into production was described as 'trifling', being no more than £385 inclusive of the cost of a water engine and the erection of stamps. Whether the promoter, Mr F. Bullin of 89 Fore Street, Plymouth Dock, succeeded in obtaining this modest capital is not known.

In 1859 the discovery was reported of a rich bed of alluvial tin about a mile above Ivybridge Viaduct. The deposit was said to be 4 to 5ft in thickness with a superficial area of nearly four acres. A proposal for working it came to nothing owing to fear of its fouling the water which supplied the paper mills of Ivybridge.[56]

One mile south-east of Ivybridge, Fillham Silver-Lead Mine (OS 125 NE), better known as Ivybridge Consols, was the most important mine of this region. Started before 1838, under grant from the provost and fellows of Eton College, working continued at intervals over a period of twenty years, during which time appreciable amounts of argentiferous lead ore were returned. Operations were suspended in December 1840 when the machinery, including a 12in condensing engine, was advertised for sale. Three years later the mine was reopened under the same management, and in October 1843 output was averaging 20 tons of ore per month, the shaft was down to 60 fathoms and preparations were in hand for further sinking. Working on this occasion lasted until March 1845 by which time sales had amounted to £4,500. The materials consisting of two water-wheels (the larger one 24ft in diameter by 10ft breast), together with 190 fathoms of flat-rods, a horse-whim, and drawing machine with crusher, are said to have realised £1,100, the sale being attended by miners from almost every part of Cornwall.[57]

Very considerable development had been carried out on the property before its closure. The shaft had been sunk to over 70 fathoms, 30 fathoms vertically and the remainder on the underlie of the lode, whilst levels extended north and south at depths of 11, 30, 43, 48, 58 and 68 fathoms, the two last for 50 and 55 fathoms northward, respectively. The south-driven levels while being more productive were short, this being due to the very restricted size of the sett. Thus in several places where good bunches of ore existed, the boundary was no more than 12 fathoms from the shaft, beyond which the ore body passed beneath the land of an adjoining owner who refused to grant. It was due to this cause more than any other that working was suspended.

Subsequently, the mine remained idle until 1852 when a new company was formed with an enlarged sett. By the summer of 1854 a 24in steam engine had been installed and the old shaft unwatered to the 30 fathom level. Meanwhile, a new vertical shaft, named Beresford's,[58] had been started and on this a 50in engine was erected in 1855 – the 24in engine being then converted for hoisting and crushing. Each of these engines did double duty, pumping and winding from both shafts respectively. By 1856 the shafts reached their maximum depths – 78 fathoms at the old shaft and 68 fathoms at Beresford's. During 1855 and 1856, lead and silver ores were returned to the value of £3,446,[59] the price of lead being then in the region of £30 a ton. Because many of the shareholders failed to meet their 'calls', it was resolved in July 1856 to abandon the cost-book system and to place the company under the Joint Stock Companies Act with a view to raising additional capital. However, due to legal difficulties this was never achieved, and in the following year the machinery and materials were put up for auction and the mine was finally abandoned.

The new Ivybridge by-pass now runs little more than half a

mile north of the mine which was recently visited by Mr Frank
Booker who contributes the following notes on its present-day
appearance:

> The engine house, built of slate rock probably quarried on
> the sett, still stands adjoining Beresford's shaft, but minus its
> roof and stack. The brick arches of the window openings,
> however, still retain traces of ornamental mouldings. Beres-
> ford's shaft, open and nearly filled with water a few years ago,
> is now blocked with rubbish. The older 70 fathom shaft in line
> with it, about 80yd due west, is apparent only from a marked
> depression, although the shaft is said to be capped. There are
> now no surface traces of the buildings housing the crushing
> plant which were prominent enough in the 1920s for C. F.
> Barclay to sketch.
>
> South-west of the 70 fathom shaft and at approximately the
> distance covered by the 190 fathoms of flat-rods is a large,
> partly filled water-wheel pit, big enough to take the 10ft
> breast overshot water-wheel sold in 1845. The leat, much
> narrower than the wheel it powered, was split into two
> sections above the mouth of the wheel-pit, thus allowing
> the water to fall more or less evenly across the full width of
> the wheel. Although now dry, the two leat courses are still
> plainly visible after the passage of more than 130 years.
>
> The dumps of the mine, particularly around Beresford's
> shaft, are much overgrown and hidden by trees, whilst the
> slatey rock [shale] of which they are composed appears to have
> rotted into a fine, black, gritty substance, superficially re-
> sembling coal dust. [Since this was written these dumps
> have been removed.]
>
> On the Ivybridge–Ermington road near the southern end of
> Wadland Wood, which adjoins the Fillham sett, is a house,
> now empty but shown on OS 125 NE as Caton Lodge.
> Tradition asserts this was used by the Fillham miners as a
> chapel and until recent years it still had a small wooden cross
> let into the gable end of the roof.

About $1\frac{1}{4}$ miles south-west of Ivybridge Consols, work was
in progress during 1854 at the Caton Copper and Silver-Lead
Mine on the banks of the River Erme. Here an adit driven 41

fathoms on a cross-course intersected two lodes of silver-lead ore, with three others containing stones of yellow copper. On one of these, Adam's Shaft was sunk 10 fathoms below the adit, from which depth an unspecified quantity of ore was raised.[60] The property was favourably reported on by Captain John Clemo of Devon Great Consols, but no further record of its working is known.

Near the prehistoric encampment on Black Down Hill 5 miles north of Kingsbridge (OS 126 SW), some grassy dumps and traces of shafts indicate the site of the Loddiswell Mine. In August 1847 the main shaft was 14 fathoms deep and in course of further sinking. Thirteen tons of ore, valued at £30 a ton, had already been sold and a further 3 tons were then being prepared at surface. The lodes were said to be large and kindly and likely to form a junction in depth. The ores consisted of barytes, white quartz, galena and grey copper, the two last in association with silver, some assays showing as much as 400oz to the ton. Although described as a copper mine,[61] lead appears to have been the predominant mineral. Working continued until October 1849 when the materials, comprising an 18ft by 12ft water-wheel, 350 fathoms of wood and 300 of iron-rods, 70 fathoms of whim rope and a similar length of chain, were advertised for sale. In his brief description of the mine, Dines refers to the remains of an engine-house. No trace of this is visible today, but his statement suggests a later working in which steam-power was employed.

In the cliff-lands extending from Bigbury Bay to Prawle Point, trials have been made in a number of places both for iron ore and copper. Shafts are, or were, recently to be seen on Thurlestone Golf Links. East of this in Hope Cove an iron mine was formerly opened in the cliffs beneath the Greystone adjacent to the village. The values, however, proved insufficient to pay the cost of working, and access to the mine was so dangerous for shipping that after one vessel had been wrecked with its cargo of ore on board, the project was abandoned.

A like fate attended the copper trial known as Easton's Mine near Bolt Tail which was started by a John Easton of Dodbrook in the year 1770. The excavations lay at the foot of an almost inaccessible cliff near the western end of Bolberry Down, adjoining Ralph's Hole.[62] The adventure did not last long, the spangled ore proving when assayed to be merely iron pyrites. The promoter gained nothing from his enterprise, 'save the empty honour of leaving the shaft his name'.[63]

Portlemouth Consols was a more pretentious affair, being the name of a full-blown company formed in 1859. The sett lay at East Portlemouth, across the river from Salcombe, and was said to contain five lodes of silver-lead in a 'highly mineralised laminated killas' extending 600 fathoms into a hill which rose to a height of 500ft. In addition, there was a champion copper lode of 'immense width similar in character to that of North Dolcoath'. By the end of 1859 a cross-cut adit had been started just above high-water mark and was calculated to give 80 fathoms of backs as it entered the hill. In the following May a correspondent wrote that the mine was being worked solely for plumbago (black lead). Contracts for the sale of this had been agreed and works were being prepared for its treatment in Lancashire and Yorkshire. 'By admeasurement they have over half a million tons discovered and containing a fair percentage of the precious metals, mica schists being their native home . . .' Apart from the possibility of finding silver and gold, the plumbago was worth £2 per ton and on this alone the mine was expected to pay dividends.[64] After this 'puff' little more was heard of the company and its shares had ceased to be quoted by August 1861.

In the early part of 1857 reports were circulated that a mine had recently been started near Prawle Point where iron lodes, 9ft to 20ft wide, were visible in the 200ft cliff. Pits sunk on the backs of these lodes for a quarter of a mile inland showed continuous mineralisation and, despite the values being erratic so near surface, the lodes appeared to be making together downwards and likely to produce 'great bodies of ore and of richer quality' in depth. Whilst the existence of iron ore in these cliffs must have long been recognised, it would seem that no attempt had previously been made to exploit them and the opening up of East Prawle Mine excited considerable interest in this quite new locality.

In 1858 a correspondent of *Mining Journal* described a visit to the workings by a 'dubious path' down the cliff. Here the ore was being blasted in adits and open-cuttings and then wheeled out to dressing-floors where the richer portions were hand-picked, whilst the refuse was thrown into the sea. It was intended to keep a stockpile of 5,000 to 6,000 tons ready at all times for shipment, and for this purpose a railway was being laid to a projecting rock in the bay, alongside which vessels of 300 tons burden could safely anchor, provided the wind was not in the south-east or south-west. It was later proposed to establish a depot at Salcombe to which the ore would be carried in the company's own barges and thence freighted to Wales. This could be done at small expense since the colliers which frequented that port would readily take it as ballast. The average run of ore contained from 35 to 40 per cent iron, worth 13s to 15s per ton delivered at Cardiff or Newport.

A short distance west of the iron workings, several caunter lodes were visible in the cliff. These were thought to contain copper ore, but being almost inaccessible they could only be seen by looking up the gullies 'which in St Just would be called zawns or "wragals"'.[65] Collins (p 559) records a sale of 300 tons of iron ore for £142 in 1858. After that year no further reports appear to have been issued, and it is probable that the mine was abandoned during the depression of the iron trade in 1859–60.

No description of the mines in this coastal area is given by Dines, nor in the *Geological Memoir*,[66] an omission excused by the *Memoir* on the curious grounds that they were the 'result of private speculation'. Through what other agency, it might be asked, was any mine started?

NOTES AND SOURCES

PART ONE (pp 17-57)

1 University of Liverpool. *A Relation of the English Mines, 1725*. Partial and extremely poor translation of the old Swedish script, Bergs Kollegium, Stockholm.
2 Still thus pronounced locally, although spelt Net Stakes on the OS map (Cornwall 30 NW). 'At Nuttstack on the Tamar there was some years ago a smelter to melt copper, tin and lead ore – now disused.' Kahlmeter (November 1724).
3 *MJ* Supplement (25 May 1844).
4 Booker, Frank. *Industrial Archaeology of the Tamar Valley* (1967).
5 Phillips and Darlington. *Records of Mining and Metallurgy* (1856).
6 Spargo (1868); Dines, p 669.
7 Hamilton, Henry. *The English Brass and Copper Industries to 1800*. Dr John Lane of Bristol (b1678), was a pioneer of the copper industry. In 1717 he established a smelting works at Landore near Swansea which continued until he was ruined by the bursting of the 'South Sea Bubble'.
8 Booker, op cit, p 139.
9 *MJ* (7 March 1846).
10 Jenkin, A. K. H. *Mines and Miners of Cornwall*, Pt 14 (1967), pp 65-9.
11 It is not known definitely which of the Bere Alston group of mines is referred to under this name.
12 *Sherborne Mercury* (6 August 1781; 7 September 1795).
13 *RIC Journal* Pt 2 (1952), Sir Arthur Russell
14 *Royal Cornwall Gazette* (13 June 1812).
15 CRO Truro MS notebook apparently belonging to Joseph Carne.
16 *Royal Cornwall Gazette* (26 May 1821; 7 September 1822).
17 *MJ* (12 December 1835).
18 *Royal Cornwall Gazette* (25 July 1851).
19 In addition to local output, the works smelted ores from Wales, Ireland, Sark, Isle of Man, and as far afield as Mexico and Australia.

143

20 Toll, R. W. *Mining Magazine* (June 1948); McDonald, Donald. *Percival Norton Johnson (1951,) passim.*

21 Watson, J. Y. 'Cornish Notes for Out-Adventurers', *MJ* (1861), pp 18-19.

22 *MJ* (July 1876).

23 *MJ* (14 October 1843; 10/24 November 1855).

24 Dines, p 683.

25 There was formerly a smelting house at Tuckermarsh Quay the sale of which was advertised in the *Royal Cornwall Gazette*, 16 January 1808.

26 *MJ* (30 May 1846).

27 *MJ* (15 February, 12 July 1851; 6 October 1855).

28 Toll, R. W. *in litt* (2 April 1958).

29 Watson, J. Y. *MJ* (3 February 1849).

30 *MJ* (1 May 1847; 3 February 1849; 23 September 1854); Dines, p 684.

31 Among the older generation of local people the mine itself is still invariably known as 'Cow-ez'.

32 *MJ* (1846-9) *passim.*

33 Murchison (1854).

34 *MJ* (16 June 1860).

35 *MJ* (29 December 1849). At a subsequent sale in 1855 the auctioneer was questioned as to the values claimed for the mine, to which he replied that although he had never before sold 'a Virtuous Lady, or any other lady, he was satisfied she was worthy of notice'. *Devonport Weekly Journal* (27 December 1855).

36 Bray, Mrs. *Tamar and Tavy*, Vol 3 (1836), pp 257-8, quoting Dr Edmund Pearse of Tavistock.

37 Toll, R. W. 'The Virtuous Lady Mine', *Western Morning News* (31 October 1956).

38 *MJ* (13 September 1845).

39 *MJ* (12 March 1859).

40 *MJ* (23 June 1860).

41 The supporting cables of the bridge came from an old battleship then under demolition at Devonport.

42 Redruth Public Library, Barclay and Toll MS.

43 *MJ* (4 December 1880).

44 Report *penes* W. J. Sleeman of Albaston in 1957, copied by A. K. H. J.

45 *MJ* (26 June 1860).

46 RIC Truro. HJ/7/6; *MJ* (13 June 1857).

47 RIC Truro. HJ/7/6.
48 Toll, R. W. *in litt,* (29 September 1953).
49 *MJ* (25 June 1853; 6 May 1854).
50 *MJ* (17 November 1855).

PART TWO (pp 59-108)

1   *MJ* (December 1845; January 1846; December 1848).
2   *MJ* (7 July 1860; 3 December 1864), *passim.*
3   *MJ* (5 December 1863; 28 November 1868); Captain Jos
    Paull, 'Report Book'. formerly *penes* the Bedford Estate Office,
    Tavistock.
4   *MJ* (18 May 1850).
5   *The Mining World and Engineering Record* (11 May 1889).
6   Dines, p 671.
7   MS at Redruth Public Library.
8   Spargo, (1868); Williams J. *Mining Directory of Cornwall and
    Devon* (1870).
9   Williams, J. *Cornwall and Devon Mining Directory* (1862).
10 Dines, p 673.
11 Bray, Mrs. *Tamar and Tavy,* Vol 3 (1836). p 254.
12 Barclay, C. F. 'Notes on the West Devon Mining District',
    Trans Roy Geolog Soc Cornwall (1930).
13 *MJ* (8 November 1879).
14 Booker, op cit, p 136.
15 *Royal Cornwall Gazette* (23 March, 22 June 1811).
16 Phillips and Darlington, op cit.
17 *MJ* (27 March 1858).
18 *MJ* (13 October 1849; 22 June 1850).
19 *MJ* Prospectus (30 October 1880).
20 CRO Exeter, Bedford Papers. Justin Brooke extract.
21 *MJ* (3 April 1858).
22 *MJ* (21 April 1860).
23 Watson, J. Y. *Cornish Notes for Out-Adventurers* (1861), p 21.
24 Spargo (1868); Williams, op cit.
25 Dines, p 690.
26 *MJ* (21 June, 5 July, 20 September 1851, *et seq*).
27 *MJ* (19 February 1853).
28 *MJ* (May 1853). Extracts by Justin Brooke.
29 *MJ* (19 January 1861).
30 Lysons. *Magna Britannia, Devon* (1822); *Royal Cornwall Gazette*
    (5 May 1810).

31 *MJ* (1 November 1856).
32 Murchison, op cit; *MJ* (23 June 1860).
33 *Plymouth and Devonport Weekly Journal* (12 April, 26 July 1855).
34 Booker, op cit, p 136.
35 Dines, p 696.
36 *MJ* (December 1868).
37 *MJ* (January 1846; January 1851); *Kelly's Directory* (1856).
38 Phillips and Darlington, op cit; Murchison (1854).
39 Collins, p 568.
40 Barclay MS.
41 CRO Exeter, 'John Swete MS' (1797-8), p 53. Extract by Justin Brooke.
42 Stoke-on-Trent, original with Josiah Wedgwood & Sons. *Common Place Book I*, 28408-39. Copy *penes* A. K. H. J.
43 Russell, Sir Arthur. *Journal of the Royal Institution of Cornwall*, Pt 2 (1952).
44 *Royal Cornwall Gazette* (18 June 1814).
45 *Royal Cornwall Gazette* (4 May 1816).
46 *Trans of the Roy Geolog Soc Cornwall*, Vol 1, pp 124-5.
47 *Royal Cornwall Gazette* (17 May 1817).
48 The reason for the mine being called Willsworthy is more difficult to explain, but it may well have formed part of the Manor of Willsworthy – manors commonly extending throughout different parishes – and sometimes more than one county.
49 *Royal Cornwall Gazette* (4 April 1818).
50 *MJ* (21 March 1846).
51 Murchison, op cit, 1856 edition, p 698.
52 Henwood. *Trans of the Roy Geolog Soc Cornwall*, Vol 5 (1843), p 475; Watson, J. Y. *Compendium of British Mining* (1843), p 56.
53 Collins, p 484.
54 *MJ* (12 February; 28 May 1870).
55 *MJ* (22 June 1861).
56 Spargo (1868); Dines, pp 699-700.
57 *MJ* (11 August 1838; 6 February 1847).
58 *Plymouth and Plymouth Dock Weekly* (2 October 1823).
59 Calvert, John. *On the Production of Gold in England*, quoted in *MJ* (10 September 1853).
60 Harris, Helen. *The Industrial Archaeology of Dartmoor*, p 220 (1968).
61 Richardson, P. H. G. MS notes of 'Mines of West Devon' (1935-9); Greeves, T.A.P. 'A Mine in the Deancombe Valley', *Trans Devonshire Association* (1969).

62 Carrington. Burt's Preface to *Dartmoor* (1826).

63 *MJ* (1838-48) *passim*.

64 *MJ* (28 April 1849).

65 *MJ* (19 April, 31 May, 1 November 1851; 29 May 1852).

66 Worth, R. Hansford. *Dartmoor* (1953), pp 303-4.

67 Exeter City Library.

68 *MJ* (13 June 1863), *et seq*.

69 *Royal Cornwall Gazette* (2 January 1808).

70 *MJ* (21 October 1848; 7 February 1852).

71 *MJ* (24 February 1877).

72 CRO Exeter, 'John Swete MS', Vol 16 (1797-8).

73 *MJ* (20 June 1846; 23 August 1862).

74 *MJ* (1849-52), *passim*; Dines, p 728 (under Devon Tin Mine).

75 *MJ* (1853-6), *passim*.

76 *MJ* (1836-40); Watson, op cit; Dines, p 728.

77 *MJ* Supplement (28 February 1874).

78 *MJ* (1852-5), *passim*.

79 *West Briton* (5 November 1891); *Parliamentary Papers*, Mineral Statistics (1892).

80 CRO Truro, 'Trestrail Coll: Hexworthy, Summary of its Later History'.

81 *The Hatchett Diary*, ed Arthur Raistrick (1967), pp 21-3.

82 CRO Truro, Davey correspondence.

83 Baring-Gould. *Devonshire Characters and Strange Events*, 2nd series (1908), p 296.

84 Henwood, op cit, pp 132, 476.

85 Spargo, 1868; Williams, op cit.

86 Broughton, D. G. 'The Birch Tor and Vitifer Tin Mining Complex', *Trans Cornish Institute of Engineers*, new series, Vol XXIV (1968-9), pp 25-49.

87 *MJ* (18 March 1848), *et seq*.

88 Broughton, op cit.

89 'London and West Country Chamber of Mines' (1904-8), p 236.

90 King's Oven, otherwise *Furnum Regis* – a medieval blowing-house.

91 Williams, op cit.

92 Broughton, op cit.

93 *MJ* (26 August 1876, 1887, p 259; 21 February 1880); Dines, p 724.

PART THREE (pp 111-42)

1 *MJ* (20 August 1853).
2 Kelly (1856); Murchison (1856).
3 *MJ* (17 January 1863).
4 *Records of Mining and Metallurgy* (1857).
5 Edwards, E. *Life of Raleigh*, Vol II, p 211.
6 *MJ* (5 November 1853).
7 Murchison (1856).
8 *MJ* (26 November 1853).
9 Report Book, Tehidy Minerals Office, Camborne.
10 Murchison (1856).
11 *MJ* (1881-9), *passim*.
12 *MJ* (2 October 1858; 31 December 1859; 28 January 1860).
13 *Royal Cornwall Gazette* (19 May 1821; 8 February 1823).
14 *MJ* (23 May 1857; 31 December 1859; 28 January 1860).
15 Spargo (1868).
16 That part of the Plym above Shaugh Bridge is sometimes styled the Cad – W. Crossing. *One Hundred Years on Dartmoor* (1901).
17 *MJ* (31 March 1838; 2 May 1840; 31 December 1859).
18 Dines, p 686.
19 Now in the Archives Department, Plymouth Central Library.
20 *Royal Cornwall Gazette* (17 July 1824).
21 *MJ* (16 July; 22 October 1836).
22 *MJ* (31 December 1859); Murchison (1854).
23 *MJ* (31 December 1859).
24 Lysons, op cit.
25 *MJ* (3 December 1859).
26 Murchison (1856).
27 *MJ* (15 September 1860).
28 *MJ* (4 August; 20 October 1855).
29 *MJ* (15 September 1860).
30 Dines, pp 686-7.
31 Not to be confused with the Hemerdon Ball Wolfram and Tin stockwork.
32 *MJ* (31 December 1856; 31 December 1859).
33 *MJ* (17 October, 14 November 1868); Kelly (1873); Dines, p 688.
34 Deed at County Museum, Truro.
35 Justin Brooke. *Mining Journal* (1850-5), extracts.
36 Barclay, C. F. *Notes on the West Devon Mining District* (1931).
37 *MJ* (31 December 1859); Kelly (1873).

38 *MJ* (27 June 1846; 10 April 1847; 31 December 1859).
39 *MJ* (7 August 1847; 31 December 1859).
40 *MJ* (30 April 1853).
41 *MJ* (9 January, 20 July, 17 August 1850; 18 October 1851; 8 May 1852).
42 *Geolog Mem Tavistock and Launceston*, p 120.
43 *MJ* (September/November 1859; 4 February 1860).
44 *MJ* (May, June, August 1850; 21 June 1851).
45 *MJ* (10 June, 14 October 1848).
46 *MJ* (26 September 1857).
47 *Plymouth and Devonport Weekly Journal* (8 August 1850); *Western Morning News* (3 December 1960).
48 Berry, A. K. 'Lost Caves of Stonehouse', *Western Morning News* (2 August 1968).
49 *West Briton* (2 July 1841).
50 *MJ* (4 August 1877).
51 *MJ* (8 May 1858).
52 *An Account of Antimony Mines of Great Britain*, MS *penes* British Museum Natural History.
53 *MJ* (9 June 1849; 23 November 1850).
54 Dines, p 689.
55 At County Museum, Truro.
56 *MJ* (17/31 December 1859).
57 *MJ* (28 October, 5 December 1843; 15 February, 18 March 1845).
58 *Plymouth Mail* (7 October 1854).
59 Murchison (1854); *MJ* (6/20 December 1856).
60 *MJ* (6 May, 19 August 1854).
61 'Near the Blackdown entrenchment is a copper mine but it is not now worked.' Fox, S. P. *Kingsbridge Estuary* (1864), p 143.
62 Shown on Bartholomew's $\frac{1}{2}$ inch map of South Devon, sheet 36.
63 Fox, S. P. *Kingsbridge and its Surroundings* (1874), pp 184-5. This volume constituted an enlarged edition of *Kingsbridge Estuary*, op cit.
64 *MJ* (27 March 1858; 31 December 1859; 4 February 1860, *et seq*).
65 *MJ* (7 February 1857; 3 April 1858).
66 *The Geology of Kingsbridge and Salcombe* (1904).

GRID REFERENCES

The following list gives the grid references for the current 2½in OS maps of the principal mines mentioned in the text.

Albert	SX 568 595	Dartmoor Consols	SX 649 728
Anderton	SX 485 723	Denham Bridge	SX 475 682
Aylesborough		Devon and	
(Eylesbarrow)	SX 599 682	Cornwall	SX 463 701
		Devon and	
Bachelor's Hall	SX 597 734	Courtenay	SX 472 717
Bedford United	SX 441 728	Devon Burra Burra	SX 514 742
Beer Alston	SX 437 647	Devon Great	
Berealston United	SX 437 678	Consols	SX 426 733
Bickleigh Vale		Devon Tin	SX 668 740
Phoenix	SX 531 642	Devon Wheal	
Birch Tor and		Buller	SX 503 670
Vitifer	SX 682 815	Duke of Cornwall	SX 668 740
Birch Tor and			
Vitifer, New	SX 682 815	Easton's	SX 681 386
Birch Tor, East	SX 694 810	Eleanor, Great	SX 732 833
Boringdon, East	SX 537 584	Emily	SX 542 498
Boringdon Park	SX 531 584	Eylesbarrow	
Bottle Hill	SX 564 587	(Aylesborough)	SX 599 682
Buller and Bertha	SX 487 696		
Buttspill	SX 437 678	Fancy	SX 437 678
		Fillham	SX 647 551
Colcharton	SX 450 730	Florence	SX 568 595
Courtenay	SX 460 724	Franco	SX 508 702
Crebor, East	SX 478 726	Friendship	SX 508 793
Crebor, South	SX 464 714	Furzehill	SX 517 692
Crebor, West	SX 452 721		
Crebor, Wheal	SX 460 724	Gatepost	SX 514 742
Crelake	SX 478 736	George and	
Crowndale	SX 470 725	Charlotte	SX 454 699
Crowndale, East	SX 478 726	George, East	SX 529 703
		Gobbett	SX 649 728
Dartmoor		Golden Dagger	SX 679 803
Consolidated	SX 599 682	Goldstreet	SX 467 664

Green Valley	SX 437 678	Rix Hill	SX 482 723
Gunnislake (East)		Robert, North	SX 513 708
& South Bedford	SX 435 719	Russell, New East	SX 464 714
		Ruth	SX 599 682
Hemerdon Consols	SX 572 588		
Hens Roost	SX 652 711	Shaugh Iron	SX 533 633
Hexworthy	SX 656 718	Sidney	SX 551 594
Hocklake	SX 469 688	Sortridge Consols	SX 510 708
Hooe, North	SX 427 661	Surprise	SX 511 740
Hooe, South	SX 425 657		
Hope Cove	SX 675 389	Tamar Consols,	
Huckworthy Bridge	SX 533 707	East (Furzehill)	SX 434 633
		Tamar Consols,	
Impham	SX 439 715	South	SX 437 645
Industry	SX 613 710	Tamar Silver-Lead	SX 425 657
Ivybridge Consols	SX 647 551	Tamar Valley, New	SX 437 678
		Tavistock Consols	SX 485 723
Julian	SX 551 597	Tavy Consols	SX 469 688
		Tavy, North	SX 471 695
Kit	SX 562 675	Tunnel	SX 431 642
Lady Bertha	SX 471 689	Virtuous Lady	SX 474 698
Lady Bertha, South	SX 477 682	Vitifer, West	SX 677 828
Little Duke	SX 471 695		
Lockridge	SX 439 665	Ward, North	SX 427 687
Loddiswell	SX 732 485	Ward, South	SX 427 677
Lopes	SX 517 633	Waterhill and	
Lopwell	SX 471 649	King's Oven	SX 676 812
Luscombe	SX 436 716	Whitchurch Down	
		Consols	SX 511 740
Maristow	SX 471 649	White Works	
Mary Hutchings	SX 565 581	(Dartmoor)	SX 613 710
		Whiteworks	
Nun's Cross	SX 604 699	(Plymouth)	SX 568 595
		Whitleigh	SX 483 598
Portlemouth		William and Mary	SX 463 701
Consols	SX 758 389	Wood	SX 478 663
Prawle, East	SX 772 353		
		Yennadon	SX 543 684
Raven Rock	SX 471 695	Yeoland Consols	SX 561 663
Reynard (Renard)	SX 588 585		

INDEX

Albert, 129
Anderton, 66
Anna Maria, 19
Ash, 66
Aylesborough (Eylesbarrow), 87–90

Bachelor's Hall, 94–5
Bedford Consols, 49
Bedford Mine, 30
Bedford, North, 18
Bedford, South, 33
Beford United, 18, 29
Bedford, Wheal, 48
Beer Alston, 36–8, 43
Berealston United, 41
Bickleigh Vale Phoenix, 117
Birch Tor and Vitifer, 101–5
Birch Tor and Vitifer, New, 104–5
Birch Tor, East, 105
Boringdon Consols, 121
Boringdon, East, 121
Boringdon Park, 121–2
Bottle Hill, 125–6
Bottle Hill, East, 126, 129
Brimpts, 95–6
Buller and Bertha, 49–50
Buttspill, 36, 41

Cann (Canal), 120
Caton, 139–40
Colcharton, 60
Collier, 81

Courtenay, 64
Crebor, 60–3
Crebor, East, 65–6
Crebor, North, 63
Crebor, South, 63–4
Crebor, West, 63
Crelake, 63, 67–9
Crowndale, 64–5
Crowndale, East, 65–6
Crowndale, South, 66

Dartmoor Consolidated, 87–90
Dartmoor United, 98
Denham Bridge, 55
Devon and Bedford, 60
Devon and Cornwall United, 35
Devon and Courtenay, 64
Devon Burra Burra, 69–70, 75
Devon Great Consols, 17–29
Devon Great Consols, East 59–60
Devon Great Tin Croft, 105
Devon Tin, 97
Devon Wheal Buller, 111–13
Devon Wheal Lopes, 119
Devonshire Silver Lead, 131–2
Duke of Cornwall, 96–7

Easton's, 141
Eleanor, Great, 107–8
Elizabeth (late Crease), 59
Emily, 135–6
Emma, 19
Eylesbarrow (Aylesborough), 87–90

152